To Troy

From Da

Christmas 1942

FAR FROM HOME

R. H. NEWMAN

*

FAR FROM HOME

*

"The night is dark, and I am far from home."
—JOHN HENRY, CARDINAL NEWMAN

J. B. LIPPINCOTT COMPANY
PHILADELPHIA   NEW YORK

INTRODUCTORY

THIS BOOK IS CRUDE. IT IS ROUGH. IT LACKS POLISH. It was written in many strange places. Parts were written in the bloody corners of hospitals and dressing stations. Parts were written in the cab of a field ambulance during daytime halts on camouflaged roads. Some of this book was written over greasy bistro tables, parts were written in brothels, some of it was thought out in the stinking dimness of a Finnish hospital train. It was written on the way to the front and on the way back from the front. It was written at the front. Many pages are written on scraps of wrapping paper, and one chapter was written on toilet paper which we had been using in Finland to roll loose tobacco from our pockets into cigarettes. Part of the manuscript was lost during the retreat from the third battle of the Marne. Another section was stolen by a phalangist informer out of a hotel room in Spain. The author was frightened while he was at work, he was bleary tired while he was at work, and many times he was drunk while he was at work. The book was started in Finland and finished in New England. It was for the major part written on the scene, in scraps and in fragments. The hates of the moment, the enthusiasms, pains, and loves of the moment govern this book. It makes no pretense toward impersonality or detachment. And even had the book been written at leisure and in comfort it would still make no pretense toward those things.

It is about war. War is a tremendous thing. It is probably the most tremendous experience a human being can undergo and remain alive. At least it is the most tremendous experience the author of this book has ever gone through. Therefore it is hard to describe the form this work has taken. It is impossible to draw a line of demarcation showing where factual truth begins and fiction leaves off because in war time what you dream at night asleep or in the day awake and what you actually go through are all reality, are all tempered by the fact of the war itself. William Saroyan describes the novel as being "many men awake through one man awake." If this book approaches that definition the author will feel he is on the right track toward learning how to write a novel. He will not, however, be satisfied. Satisfaction has no place in creative work. Satisfaction is a kind of death. It is the commonest disease of which writers die.

This is not a history. Its main concern is not events, but people. And the author only hopes that it in some measure reflects the courage and the gallantry with which the Finnish people and the people of France faced tragedy and disaster. They faced this in different ways. But with no less courage on either part. In Finland there was unity of purpose. In France there was betrayal. Finland was an athlete in top form. France had been out of training over too long a period. Finland was a spiritual victory for democracy. France was a tragedy demonstrating what can happen to democracy when liberty lies unguarded.

The war still goes on. It is spreading. And it must be faced that universal participation in this catastrophe is inevitable. It can only be this way. This dreadful road is the only one which lies before us toward the final settlement of the issues at stake. These are bloody times, but they are also times of justice, rough as it may be. Everything that has happened was pre-ordained, was preached, editorialized, and mouthed from every semblance of a rostrum for over twenty years. And still something kept the people of the world from settling their problems in peace. It may well be that there was no peaceful settlement. Slavery and freedom are diametrically opposed. And violence may be the only conclusion. If the aggressor does not respond to reason he must be stamped out. And to say we have not a quarrel with all who follow the men who lead them toward crime, is an absurdity. This method of reasoning has been followed before. It led from Versailles to Dunquerque.

What lies before us is a sad and bloody task. Let us not lose our dignity in carrying it out. Let us do what we have to do. But let us not allow our hate to spread among ourselves and let us remember that it is the young men who will give their lives and let us remember further that for those who have not yet lived their young lives there is nothing worse than dying. Let us not make our destiny mawkish with false sentimentality. Let those who stay at home not become the pathetic clowns many of them became in the years 1917–1918. The young will die and fight and suffer. They always have. Let us not, as many have already started, prod them with invective because they are slow to make their wills.

We know our duty. No one has allowed us to forget it in the twenty odd years which have elapsed since our birth. We will go because we see the issues more clearly than our elders. Please do

not try and shame us into going with white feath-
ers and kisses from pretty girls. These bandstand
trappings have no place in the sadness, the horror,
and the pain which lie ahead of the young genera-
tion.

And in the end, which must be made to justify
the means, the dead must have the only memorial
worth the sacrifice they will have made . . . a
lasting peace.

Norwell, Massachusetts
September, 1940

FAR FROM HOME

I

What passing-bells for these who died as cattle?
Only the monstrous anger of the guns,
Only the stuttering rifles' rapid rattle,
Can patter out their hasty orisons.
                                    —WILFRED OWEN

THERE WAS THE ADVANCE AND THERE WAS THE RE-
treat. And they moved on opposite sides of the
same road. It was a very dark night. There was no
moon and there were no stars. It seemed as if all
the hope had gone out of the world and all the
pity, leaving only the oily cotton batting darkness
and the fear curling at the bottom of your stomach.
The lights from fleeing civilian cars blinded you
and made you drive into other cars. Sometimes
you drove into other cars on purpose just because
you were angry and tired and a little drunk and a
little hungry. Sometimes you even cried deep down
inside yourself. But when you can see all that's
left of France staggering down one side of a road
and you're moving toward what smashed them
with all that's left of Poland and you're an Ameri-

15

can only maybe you won't ever see it again, then what the hell do you care if you cry a little.

You were alone in your car and there weren't even any lights to light up the dashboard. There weren't even any stars to light up the sky. There were only the flares they sent to light you up for the bombing planes. There was only the glare of Epernay burning behind a hill far off to the right.

It wasn't raining but there was the feeling of its being a rainy night. There was also the feeling of its being the last night on earth. The last night for everybody . . . for Hitler and Pétain and Roosevelt and Hoover and Shirley Temple and Charlie McCarthy and especially yourself.

Through towns you drove on the sidewalk. You hit anything that got in your way. There was one time when you hit one of the motorcycle links. When you stopped to look back you could see the soldier standing up swearing in the road. The motorcycle was on its side with the wheel spinning top speed. He was trying to stop it.

"Ça va, mon vieux?"

"Ça va, mon putain."

"For Christ's sake get going. We'll lose the convoy."

You couldn't break convoy. Not for anything. Already you'd lost the second regiment and were going up half strength to the attack. All the orders were bitched up. Fifth column. Stupidity. Every order conflicted with every preceding one. No one knew where they were going. Or what time the attack was for. Somewhere ahead. Up toward Epernay. So the column moved ahead. The trucks and armored cars and tanks and motorcycles with machine-gunners in the sidecars and the American ambulances, they all moved ahead toward the jagged flames behind the hill far off to the right.

Sometimes the traffic was snarled and there were halts. Sometimes for over an hour. Then you'd all stand out in the road and pass bottles to each other. That was good. It was good to have people around you. Better than sitting alone in the cab of your ambulance thinking out your life, squinting at the white spot painted on the car ahead of you. Thinking over your life, you always did that those nights. All the girls you'd known and all the places you'd been . . . all the books you'd read and all the conversations you'd had. There were many girls. Most of them were probably married by now. They were home listening to Raymond Gram Swing. Well, you wished them luck. Lots of it. And there were many books and most of them were wrong. You knew that now.

And there were so many places . . . there had

been Finland. How many years ago? Three months. What the hell were you doing there? What the hell were you doing here for that matter?

Finland is Finlandia and Finlandia is Finland. Finland is the curve of a snowy road at dawn. The snow is packed hard and glistens and the sky is coppered blue and rusty with the rising sun and the pines are stiff and tall. It is a snowy road at dawn with a sleigh swinging high up around the top of a curve and the horses slipping and panting frosted breath. It is the beginning swoop down a slope on skis. It is the smell of the dried birch switches in the steam of the sauna. It is the grey shine of a pukko blade. It is a thin line of men dressed in white waiting in the snowy forest dawn for the tanks to come. It is the Karelian song and the Porilaisten March. It is frozen lakes. And the Lottas. It is Suomussalmi and Kemmi and Syskjarvi and Sala. . . .

It was very quiet in the woods that day after the shelling had stopped. While there had been the shelling it had seemed there was nothing in the world but the sound of the shells coming ten to the minute, cushioning over the line with a shriek like chalk on the blackboard and bursting in the tops of

—

the trees. But after the shelling stopped, the stillness set in and lay soft through the woods like the
snow and all you could hear was the swish swish
of your skis as you moved along behind the trail
of blood which spattered reddish between the ski
tracks you were following.

It was a grey afternoon. The pine trees stood stiff
and straight on either side of you. They were iced
and snowed over, but in spots the green shown
through darkly and the trees were tall and black
and naked against the snow in the half light of this
winter dusk. Far off to the left you could hear the
choked riveting noise of a machine gun and once
in a while there were isolated shell bursts. But they
were so far off that they sounded dry and sharp like
rifle bullets.

When the blood spots began to be thicker, the ski
tracks became more uncertain. They were wider on
one side and you could see that the man ahead of
you was having a hard time keeping his right leg
from spread-eagling out from under him. You were
sure it was a wounded Finn up there ahead. A Russian could never have come that far and Russians
do not know how to ski.

Finally you came to the end of the woods. The
ground spilled sharply into a valley and rose again
in a slow slope on the other side and at the top of

the slope was a cabin. The blood was very thick and
here at the dip into the valley there was a great
threshing about of the snow as if the man ahead
had fallen.

You came out of the woods and looked across the
valley to the hills. You were heavy with sweat. You
had come ten kilometers after this trail of blood.
You shoved with the ski poles and felt the snow slip
out under you. You slid easily at first and then began to rush faster and faster into the curve of the
slope as you bent closer to the ground. You began
to brake yourself with the poles like the Finns did.
At first when you moved your wrists down to shove
the tips of the poles into the snow behind you,
there was a jerk and you thought you would fall,
so you let up on the braking and were all right
again. You made a snow plow and a turn at the
bottom and started climbing on a slant. You wanted
to come up along one side of the cabin just in case
it was a wounded Russian who knew how to ski.
You were carrying a gun and a long bladed knife
and you made sure you knew exactly where each
of them was. When the hill steepened you began
to slip and turned again and came up the hill side-
ways, placing the poles very carefully before each
step and being sure of their position. By this time
there was a definite line of blood wavering up the

slope in large looping lines.

You got to the top and took a long breath. Then, loosening the pistol in its holster, you pushed the holster around on the belt until it hung straight over your right thigh.

You moved ahead very slowly to the cabin. You could feel your heart butting against your ribs and, for a moment, you thought you would be sick. But you weren't. You undid the binding and stepped out of your skis. Your legs went down into the snow up to your thighs and you foundered until you were back on the thin spine of hard ground which made a path to the cabin door. You started to draw your gun, but you stopped when you saw the soldier.

The soldier was lying face down in the snow. His skis were off. He had slipped out of them when he fell. Some Finns wear only one strap across the toe of their hooked boots for a ski binding and when the soldier had fallen he had slipped right out of them. The soldier had been hit in the back by a shell splinter. There was a great rip through his clothes and the blood was crusted far around it and the edges of the rip were soaked in blood which hadn't hardened yet in the cold. The soldier was wearing the hooded top to a white snow suit, but it was colored rust by this time.

You knelt next to the soldier. The soldier was

breathing in bubbling grunts. But he was not unconscious. He opened his eyes when he was turned
over and an expression of annoyance went over his
face when he saw the red crosses on the first aid
boxes.

"Fools," the soldier said, "all doctors are fools."
The soldier's voice was very faint and far away as
if you both might be in different places talking to
one another over a bad telephone connection.

His face was stained with powder, but under this
coal dusty blackness he was waxy pale. The soldier
was very young. Twenty maybe at the most. He was
extremely young and he was going to die very soon.

"The house," he murmured, "the house."

You began to move him toward the cabin, trying
not to cause him any extra pain, but outside of that
it did not matter how he was moved. He was too far
gone for that to be important.

The cabin was deserted, but it gave signs of having recently been lived in. It had a hurried evacuated look. Many houses had that. The look of the
hasty choice made of what to take along. People trying to decide in a hurry what things were most precious to them out of the things they owned. These
things made you guess the house had been abandoned while the Russians were still advancing.
There were some few shabby pieces of furniture

and some rusted pots and pans. There was a faded calendar on the wall turned to the page for December. It was now February.

You laid the soldier as carefully as possible on a dirty boxlike sofa. The soldier's eyes were closed again. You placed him on his side and began to swab compresses over the wound. There was no reason for doing it, but you felt you had to do something. After you had been doing this for a few minutes your hands were bloody to the wrists.

The soldier's eyes fluttered open. You could see that already they had that appearance of receding back into the skull which is peculiar to the dying, and you saw that the soldier's skin was taking on that greyish waxed color which is also a part of death.

You took out a pack of cigarettes and pointed to them. The soldier nodded. You lighted a cigarette and placed it gently between the soldier's lips. From time to time you would withdraw the cigarette from the soldier's mouth so that he might blow out or inhale the smoke. You moved as if you were standing on tiptoes. You were not so used to war that death didn't fill you with a childlike awe. It made you feel small and full of things carried over from your childhood. You tried to remember some prayer for the dead, but you couldn't. This made you angry with yourself and also a little frightened. A man should not forget such things, you told yourself.

The soldier opened his eyes all the way. The cigarette seemed to have given him some new energy. Or, you thought, maybe just at the end of his existence a man's life flows out of him in a sudden quickening surge, as in a fountain pen the ink flows more strongly just before the pen goes dry.

The soldier pointed to himself and then gestured toward the walls of the cabin. You shrugged that you did not understand and this seemed to distress the soldier. He pointed to the pocket of his uniform. You reached into the pocket. You took out a pack of papers and pictures. There was a snapshot of the soldier standing in the center of a group of girls in summer dresses. The soldier was holding an accordion. There was a snapshot of the soldier standing naked in the snow holding a block of ice.

"Sauna." The soldier murmured to explain that this photograph had been taken just after he had come from the Finnish bath where steam is produced by pouring water over hot stones and your body becomes so heated that for a few seconds you can roll naked in the snow without feeling anything. Then there was the photograph of a house. You looked at it for a long time. You felt you had seen it before and you wondered where. Then suddenly you realized you were sitting in it. This was the soldier's home.

The feeling of awe in you became so tremendous that you felt it would choke you. You turned your head away. There was a tightening pain in your chest and throat.

"Oh Jesus," you said softly, "Oh Jesus, Mary, and Joseph."

When you turned back you saw the soldier looking weakly around the walls of the cabin. There was a satisfied smile on the soldier's face as quietly and quickly and comfortably he began to die. It did not take him long and at the end he was still smiling the smile of one who has come a long way home to the things he has always known and has carried with him wherever he had to go.

And you, still remembering things carried with you from some place far back and far away, crossed yourself as you left the cabin.

When you came outside you saw that it had begun to snow again and this clean new snow lay over everything. It drifted against the sides of the cabin and cottoned thickly in the tops of the trees. It stretched out over the earth farther than a man could think. And it was all there was in that place except for the broken thunder of the guns which

echoed from the horizon far back beyond the tips
of the tallest pine trees. . . .

Yes, there was Finland and Finland was Finlandia. It was Mannerheim. It was Kallio. It was
Tanner. It was Sibelius. It was the station in Helsinki and the restaurant you used to like in Sortavala. You had tea with jam in it at that restaurant
and learned to say "Kuinko voite," then when they
bombed the place the restaurant caved in on top of
the bank below it and the pots and pans lay mixed
up with the adding machines and safety deposit
boxes. . . .

There was always Finland to think about during
halts in France. You could try to get courage from
remembering it. From remembering them. You
could try for courage telling about it to the
others. . . .

The time you sat in the chief doctor's office waiting for him. He had come into the room slowly,
walking as an old man does. But he was not old. It
was only that he was very tired. So tired in fact that
he wondered was it possible for him to go on much
longer as he was going on now.

He had pulled back the hood of his white snow
suit and he had sat down heavily in the chair behind
his desk. Just as he had been about to settle back

he had risen again. This time he removed the map case which was slung over his left shoulder and the belt which crossed over his right shoulder. There was a gun hanging to the belt, a long-barreled parabellum pistol in a wooden holster and there was a slightly curving bladed Finnish knife in a tooled leather sheaf. The captain hung these things upon a peg on the wall and sat down again after he had first lighted a cigarette.

"Well?" He looked at you with a sad smile. The sad smile was very much a part of this captain's face.

"Two more of them died last night," you said.

"After I left?"

"Yes, sir. After you left."

"That makes six."

"Seven, sir. There was the belly wound."

"He died in the ambulance," the captain said sharply. "He doesn't count."

"Yes, sir."

"We must always be exact," the captain told you. "We must keep little things like that straight in our minds. Some day we may want to make an accounting of it."

"Yes, sir."

"How many of them died on the table?"

"Four, sir."

The captain frowned. "I can only account for

three," he said. "The two chest wounds and the fractured skull, which wasn't a skull really," he went on in an academic way, "but more the fragments of a skull. There was nothing to do but let the man die. You understand?"

"Yes, sir."

"We are so constructed," the captain continued, "that we cannot function without a skull. You follow me?"

"Yes, sir."

"And a defective skull is better than no skull at all. Three died on the table. Very well."

"Four, sir." You corrected him gently.

"I cannot account for the fourth. You must be mistaken."

"The one who was frozen. He died on the table."

"Ah, yes," the captain nodded. "But," he added triumphantly, "we cannot really claim him either. The cold got him. Neither we nor the Russians had a thing to do with it. It was merely a matter of a lowering of the temperature."

"I see, sir." You were glad the captain had gotten around it that way, the death rate in the station was becoming alarmingly high. The captain felt responsible for it and it worried him.

"Here, take one." The captain handed you a cigarette from a box on his desk.

You fitted it into a short wooden holder.

"The cars are well hidden?" he asked.

"Yes, sir. We moved them yesterday. Into the woods."

"Fine. And the red crosses?"

"We painted them out."

"Fine. How often are you having them warmed?"

"Every hour, sir, until the cold breaks."

"Fine." He acted as if he kept searching his mind for things to say. Anything to keep the conversation going. "There must be no more new ski trails," he said. "Will you ask the sergeant major to post a notice to that effect?"

"Yes, sir."

"The men must keep to the road or through the woods. But no new trails across the fields. They can be seen from the air."

"Yes, sir."

Suddenly he leaned across the desk to you. "Listen," he said. "Have you ever wanted to yell? Or laugh very loudly at the wrong moment? Has your chest ever been full of laughter at the wrong time . . . when someone has just died . . . and when you tried to laugh the laughter wouldn't come and all that happened was your hands began to shake?"

You nodded, but you did not reply.

"No. Not yet for you," the captain said. "It happens to me many times. It happens to me in the operating room. That is very bad."

"Yes, sir."

"I am cracking," the captain said. "Does that surprise you? It surprises me. I am covered with blood and bits of people's insides and I am cracking. All these bits of skull and intestines and flesh are in my food and tea and eyes and my ears and my sleep. There is a line in your Shakespeare which fits this, but I cannot recall it at this moment. How soon do you think it will take before I crack completely?"

"You won't crack, sir." You wished the captain would stop speaking this way. There was something nakedly unpleasant about it.

"No?" He said this in a mocking tone.

"No, sir."

"And why not?"

"It is impossible. You must get more sleep, sir."

"And you think that this will avert the catastrophe. That it will prevent me from beginning to bark like a dog or howl like a wolf or something else that might be completely stupid."

"Yes, sir. Sleep. That's all. You can't crack. But you must sleep."

"There is a line in Shakespeare which fits that also," the captain said. "Shakespeare outdates the Freudians by several centuries. I tell you that and

I am a doctor. It is too bad. When I was a lieutenant I could have howled away. Now I am a captain and I must not. It is not fair." He shrugged. "No," he said, "I won't crack. You may post a notice to that effect." He smiled sadly again. "But," he went on, "I won't sleep either."

"Yes, sir."

"You may go now."

"Yes, sir." You rose and clicked your heels and went out.

The captain was right. He did not crack. And he did not sleep, either. He tried to sleep, however. And when he found he couldn't his face stopped smiling and began to twitch. He was a fine captain and he hung on until the very end. He never turned his back as other captains have done in other armies.

No one ever turned his back in that army. And it was good to think about later on in France.

There on the road you thought about those things. The others were passing the bottle around and sometimes it came to you and then there was the sudden hot jerk of the liquor in the bottom of your stomach.

The retreat still flowed by thickly. Some of the civilian refugees slept by the side of the road. They just lay where they dropped and huddled together to sleep.

You walked ahead up the line to see what was happening. There was a hopeless tangle of traffic. It would be impossible to move for at least an hour. There were no orders. They were balled up again. The major went off on a motorcycle to find out what was happening ahead. Everybody stood around asking questions in Polish and in French and in English.

You were told to go back to your car and try for some sleep while you waited.

Suddenly it seemed as if you'd done nothing else the past year but wait for things to happen. It was the same in Finland. Nights lying places waiting for things to happen you had gotten into this habit of going over your life so very carefully, piece by piece, bit by bit. In the beginning it had all begun with your trying to remember the name of some song which had been popular years back when you were in school. You kept trying to remember what you had done in the middle time between when you had left school and when you had gone to war. It was such a short time that you almost cried when you thought of it. But this thinking had brought things back until now you had the whole sequence of them sliding along nightly through your brain like a smoothly oiled factory belt which moved always forward in the same slow complete circuit.

There was the night with Einar. Lying in the woods looking ahead at the hard packed snow shining along the road beyond the forest, trying to imagine what the Russian tanks would look like when they came along that road at dawn. But you couldn't. You could only think of girls you had known back in America and places you had been.

"Einar."

He rolled over on his side. "Yes? What is it?"

"After the war let's go to America together. You'd like it there."

"Fine," Einar said. "Fine."

"There are a lot of Finns in America."

"I know," Einar said. "I have an uncle in Detroit." Einar spoke very good English and pronounced Detroit almost correctly.

"We could go fishing, Einar."

"Fine."

"How's the fishing in Finland?"

"Very good, but it's better in Norway. How's the fishing in America?"

"Very good, but it's better in Canada."

"Oh."

"And in Scotland and in Ireland."

"Oh," Einar said again. He had never been out of Finland except to go to Norway or Sweden and when you spoke of places where you had been and he hadn't, his voice took on the same peculiar tone.

You rolled over on your back and could feel the snow biting your neck and so you pulled the hood of your snow suit higher. You tried very hard to picture what it would be like in the morning when the tanks came. First there was the man ahead. The man in the hole in the road. This man had a crow-bar and it was his job to jam this crow-bar at the tank and spring the tread so that the tank would have to stop. Then the man would throw lighted petrol into the tank and other men would do the same or would open up with anti-tank guns. You had talked a long time with this man. He did not seem to be particularly impressed by his work. He said that he was too low in the road for the tank gunners to hit him. But you did not believe this.

"Einar."

"Yes?"

"I'd like to eat a really fine meal right now. Wouldn't you?"

"I'm not hungry," Einar said.

"Neither am I. But I'd like to eat escargots. You know, snails."

"I know," Einar said. "But I don't think I'd like them."

"Everybody says that, but they're one of those things. One of those really good things. And I'd like a good chateaubriand."

"Stop talking about food," Einar said. "What's the use?"

"I like eating. It's good. Like fishing."

"Everything's like fishing with you."

"Music, too. That's like fishing. And skiing, you know?"

"I know," Einar said.

"What's wrong, Einar?"

"Nothing."

"We'll pull it off. Don't worry."

"I'm not worrying."

Einar was the transport lieutenant in charge of the ambulances and this was the first show of any kind where he had been in complete charge. You were working farther up than you had ever worked before. Naturally Einar was a little worried.

"Have a cigarette, Einar. There's a pack of Saimas in the map case."

Saimas were the best of the issue cigarettes. North States were better and so were Twenty Golds, but you couldn't get them any more. And Saimas were better than "whistles" which had an inch cardboard holder pasted to the end of them.

You could hear the Russian artillery from far off. The Russian shells were landing short. Landing so short, in fact, that they must be bursting inside the

Russian lines. You shivered. That seemed so terribly like murder. Of course, it was better than to have the shells landing inside of the Finnish lines. But it was certainly no way to attack. To start off by shelling your own side seemed indecent. Those damned Russians. Everyone felt it. No matter how you hated them for what they'd done, you hated them even more for the sloppy stupid amateurs they were. The whole conscripted pressed-into-service mass of them. They might have known all about Marx and Engels, but they certainly should have taken a little time off to learn about their own thirty-seven millimeter guns.

You tried to remember how long this attack had been going on. Weeks it seemed. But then it wasn't an attack really. They had surrounded this Russian division and slowly like freezing snow they had tightened the circle, battering back every attempt of the Russians to break through or of Russian reinforcements to get to the division. It was an important operation. If the Russians did break through they would have a straight road to Sortavala and could get at the Karelian Isthmus from the back. There was only this thin circle stopping them. So this division had to be wiped out. Now it looked as if the end had come. The Russians were making one last try. And soon enough, too. Six weeks were no picnic. It was too long a time to go borrowing on your luck, too long. You shivered again.

"Yes sir," you said. "Escargots. I know a girl who loves them."

"Do you?" Einar said. "What's she like?"

"I don't know any more. I know what she was like. But I don't know if it still goes. You know?"

"Why didn't you get married?" Einar said.

"Why?"

"It's what you do," Einar said.

"Not where I come from."

"America is funny," Einar said.

"Where I come from isn't exactly America."

"New York," Einar said. "That's America."

"Only in the geography books. Besides it's more than New York where I came from. It's also Chicago and a school in New Hampshire and it's parts of Paris and some pubs in London like the Lord Belgrave. You pick out your own chop there, Einar."

"Do you?"

"Sure." You felt like talking now. That was one thing in your life that always worked. Talking. You could talk it all out of you when it got too bad. "And there's the Saracen's Head at Beaconsfield. That's where Disraeli came from."

"Where do you come from?" Einar asked.

"I don't know. There's Saint Tropez. That's a little place south in France where there's the whitest lighthouse you ever saw and the bluest water and Saint Maxime like pink cake crumbs across the water and you run around in fisherman's clothes and espadrilles and only go there in the spring and fall because terrible people go there in the summer. And there's the mistral and it rattles shutters down the street and the rain pastes the walls wet with colors leaking down from posters and the mistral gives people headaches only I don't believe that. That's where I come from and it's all sun and vineyards before the grapes come and after the grapes are gone and the vines are twisty black roots against tan earth and the houses are pink and the roofs are red and everybody's skin is sunburnt brown."

"Yes?" Einar said and you could see that he wanted you to go on talking this time.

"Yes. And the vin blanc du pays is only six francs a liter and it turns your tongue black if you drink too much of it. And there's Paris, too. That's where I come from. There's the sun in the mornings shining on all the bad taste gilt at the Pont Alexandre and exploding like rainbows on the glass pigeons at the Rond Point and in the spring when it rains you can sit out in front of Weber's on the Rue Royale and taste the spring on your tongue like the crushed petals of violets. That sounds damned silly. And people shouldn't talk this way. But it's true. And I can talk any damned way I want from now on. Can't I, Einar?"

"Sure you can," Einar said.

"On account of Sala and Kemmi I can say anything I want. Huh, Einar?"

"Sure."

"No more monosyllables, Einar. They're out. They were silly to begin with. Now they're kaput. Huh, Einar?"

"Yes," Einar said. "Yes."

"You know where I come from?"

"You just told me." There was laughter in Einar's voice for the first time since he had gotten the second star to wear on his collar.

"The hell I have. I haven't even begun. There's coming to Ireland in the morning. It's all islands just floating and lights burning along the land at places like Clonakilty Bay and Gallows Head. Then the night goes bang and cracks and it's all pale green sky and long low purple wings of cloud and the last star and gulls wheeling over the ship like bombing planes and the sky goes bang again and it's all crazy red with the sunrise and the hills are black against it and the gulls' wings flash pink in it. People shouldn't talk this way, but I can on account of what we know. Huh, Einar?"

"That's it," Einar agreed.

"It's all green and furry. And there's the cathedral like a paper cutout on top of a hill. And there's Dublin and Cork and the dusk comes in Cork like ropy blue smoke and women creep along the streets in black shawls and you hear the Shandon bells. And in Dublin the dusk is fine, too. And all the city swirls against the base of Nelson pillar and farther down toward Grafton Street the pillars at the Bank of Ireland shine out like white bones against the darkness and wind is the coldest wind you ever felt. It comes like a razor blade down from the Wicklow mountains, and I don't give a hoot in hell how people should talk. And there's New York. Only you can't talk about that. You can talk about snow falling down across the Art Institute lions in Chicago in the evenings in winter. But New York, no. It's too much. It's like trying to talk about Beethoven."

"Or fishing?" Einar put in.

"Or fishing."

"What about that girl?" Einar said. "You should have married that girl."

"Yeah. That would have been just dandy."

You looked around back of you into the woods. The sky was greying milky with the dawn. You

could see the tents of the Finnish platoons spreading out black like blots of ink soaked into the snow
and you could see men now in white snow suits
lying in the snow with automatic rifles and
machine-guns waiting for the attack to come crashing down on them.

"What was she like?" Einar asked again.

"I don't know. She liked Chanel Five and escargots and she wore grey flannel slacks by Creed
and she had hair that curled up at the ends like a
boy's cap, and she said darling in eighteen syllables
and you fainted inside with each one. But that's no
help. How the hell do I know what she was like?
To hell with you."

"All right," Einar said. "To hell with me. You
better warm those motors. Then come back and tell
me more about that girl."

You shook your head. While you had talked you
had felt drunk. Now you had the hangover and
didn't want to talk any more.

The leather seat of the Citroën was freezing cold.
When you pulled the starter the engine turned
over and then you gave her gas and got her running
and went down the line doing the same to the others
. . . gas vapor steamed white from the exhausts
and up ahead toward Russia the shelling was louder
and the shells were beginning to land close. It was

almost time for the tanks.

A shell burst over your head in the trees. Chanel Five. Creed. Darling. Hair like a boy's cap curling up at the ends. Suddenly you felt that all your life for twenty-five years you had been running, but now you'd tripped and fallen and couldn't run any farther.

Those were the Russian tanks. And now you were waiting for the German tanks. Einar was dead. And so were the others, most of them. The whole show was almost over now. Nothing left to do but think sadly while you waited for it to finish. Nothing left to do but to remember the things that had been fun. Don't ever think of what might happen. Going under or surviving are both pretty horrible thoughts. Think back. Don't think ahead. Look at all the pretty pictures in your brain. Football Saturdays in Cambridge and at Exeter and everywhere else. Smoke from leaves burning in the air. Whiskey smells in the air. Bands and the boomf at the kickoff and all the drums beating when there was a touchdown and afterwards safe and smug, having fun. Nothing could touch you. And you did exactly what you wanted. Well, you were paying for it now. But what wonderful thoughts they had been. . . .

And to live in a white house and lean against a

stone fence looking out over the hills toward Boston
or to come home from fishing or shooting and your
girl is waiting for you and she says hello and you
say hello and you go into your house and sit by a
fire with the firelight jellying amber in the whiskey
and you sit there talking or not talking or listening
to music or not listening to anything but just being
alone and safe in your love for each other. . . .

Sitting on that path in the Bois the night it
rained and there was an alerte. There was the
D.C.A. bursting yellow over the horizon of Paris
and you sat there talking and softly holding hands
and the rain spatted on the dead leaves that autumn
night in the Bois.

"You don't believe in it," she kept saying.
"You've always said you didn't believe in it."

"I know. That's what I said."

"But," her voice was sad, "you're doing it anyway. I don't understand," she said. "It isn't your
fight. You're neutral. America's neutral."

"I'm not neutral."

"But they bomb ambulances. They machine-gun
them."

"I know."

"I should think you'd have more sense than to
rush off and get killed."

"Look."

"Yes."

"Do me a big favor, please. Don't talk about getting killed. It makes me feel funny. Please, don't talk about bombs or machine-guns. Talk about baseball or the Davis cup. Talk about Joe Louis. Let's go dancing."

"We can't. It's against the law."

"I want to hear music. I want to hear one-man music. Something clean and lonely and very pure like Louis Armstrong. I feel lonely. We're in love and they passed a law against dancing."

"Listen," she said, "love is Romeo and Juliet and Pelleas and Melisande. And in church they say that Christ is love. It isn't us. We're too small. It isn't a girl like me and a soldier. It's shepherds and nymphs. Even the poets don't write about girls like me and people like you."

"We own the earth."

"I don't want to own the earth," she said. "I only want our little part of it. That's all."

"Hell. Let's talk about something else. Take poetry. Take Donne. When I have done I have not done. That's Donne and what's done is done and cannot be undone. That's Shakespeare."

"Don't be clever. Please don't be clever. I can't stand that."

"O.K. Let's take you for example. You're beautiful. You're lovely."

"I don't like that either," she said. "It's non-
sense."

"There's no such thing as beauty anyway. Everything's beautiful. The sun is and so is the S in the
sign for Fifty-Seventh Street. It's a terrific little
chunk of motion. Everything's beautiful. There's
no such thing."

"Am I like that?"

"You're like everything. You're beautiful and
calm and wise. You're like a great mysterious
thought about God."

"Thank you," she said. "I was afraid you'd say
something trite about my eyes being like stars or
something."

"Let's get out of here. The planes are gone."

"Darling, let's go to where I live."

"We'd better not. That makes it too much like
the movies. Mickey Mouse and Carole Lombard.
Poor boy and he's so young too."

"Don't say that."

"But it's true."

"Darling." She put her hand on yours. "It isn't
that way. Not really."

"The hell it isn't."

"It's only a few more days, darling. We can pre-
tend we're married and that we're having a fine life
together. Just for those few days."

"They did that in Seventh Heaven. Hi, Janet
Gaynor."

"It's not that way."

"Sure it is. The only difference is that the movies
do it better. Their sets are better in Hollywood.
No kidding. I saw that at Sarreguemines. The sets
were better in All Quiet on the Western Front."

"Don't make it that way," she said.

"Don't blame me. Blame Leo the Lion."

That was just before you left for Finland. And
when you came back she was gone. You hadn't
thought it would be that way. You'd planned meeting her so carefully. Thought about it so much.
Nights when you didn't know what would happen
you dreamed it. You thought about it that time
riding on the hospital train. They played the
phonograph, the doctor and the head Lotta. Liszt
and Sibelius. Three days it went on that way. And
all around you were the dim shapes of men and the
white of the bandages and the smell of drying
clothes and dried blood and infected guts and ski
wax and you dreamed on and on for three days
lying there while they played the phonograph.
Then you got back to Paris when that war was over

and she wasn't there any more.

That was the terrible part. You wandered and got drunk and got in fights up in Montmartre. One night you had a girl from some place and you were mean and nasty and she cried and told you to be gentle and you said you'd forgotten how and you walked up and down streets in Paris and this girl followed along crying and telling you to be gentle. It was terrible.

You'd planned it all so carefully. You'd seen the two of you doing so many wonderful things together. You'd seen yourself teaching her what you knew about salmon fishing. Standing out in the stream where Black Brook swirls out white over the stones and comes whirling into the Mirimachi. You'd seen yourselves skiing. Seen her coming fast down a slope crouching low with her hair rushing back in the slip stream of the wind and the snow feathering up from the skis. At Kitzbühel or Davos or Mont Tremblant. Oh yes, they'd been lovely thoughts.

But they didn't come out. It was all very disappointing. Like coming home from school for vacations. And you were glad when they canceled all leaves and you had to go back to the army.

It's better in the movies. Everyone knows that. Take Greta Garbo. Take Madeleine Carroll. Take

Katharine Hepburn. There was a little Finn captain who liked Katharine Hepburn. That had been a funny thing that day you met him. You had driven up to the front through the grey dusk of a snowy day. The road was rutted and packed with hard shiny snow and the car skidded high on the sides of curves. The curves were marked by red lanterns on posts, but the windows were frosted and you could not see the lanterns. You could only tell the car was going around the curves by the difference in the skidding.

When you'd stopped at the advance medical post, this captain met you in the center of the road and you followed him off into the woods to one of the half-tent half-dugouts that the platoons lived in.

The inside of the tent was fuggy with heat from a stove dug down deep into the earth at the center. Each platoon had its own tent and the men slept on straw piled onto wooden platforms built up a foot or so from the ground. You went with the captain down some narrow steps into the dugout which was bright and clean with shelves built into the wall and the props which held the earth back were made of clean strong-smelling pine.

You sat there all afternoon talking and smoking with the captain. He was anxious to talk about New York. He had been there during the summer to

do something for the Finnish exhibit at the World's
Fair and would talk about nothing else but Twenty
One and the Stork Club and Billy Rose's. He liked
New York. He liked Americans. He was glad you
were there and he hoped you wouldn't get hurt. He
had seen many plays in New York. He thought
Tallulah Bankhead was wonderful. But Katharine
Hepburn was the kind of girl he would like to
marry if he hadn't already a wife.

Then proudly he opened his map case and began thumbing through it.

"Sala," he muttered, "Suomussalmi, the Isthmus,
the Kemmi River." He had been on many fronts,
this captain. And he kept thumbing through the
maps of them until he found what he was looking
for. "Aha," he said finally, "here it is."

It was a theatre program and he leafed through
it until he came to a picture of Katharine Hepburn.
It was autographed. It said, "Yours Truly . . .
Katharine Hepburn."

"She is very fine," he said.

Then he replaced the picture and the maps.
Sala, Suomussalmi, the Isthmus, the Kemmi River,
Yours Truly . . . Katharine Hepburn.

Afterwards you both walked out on the road to
do the business you had come for. You walked
about five hundred meters. Right toward Russia.

The captain laughed. "It is cheaper than Intourist," he said. "The grand tour."

When you had finished, the captain saw you into the car again. As you left he stuck his head in through the window. "Some day," he said emphatically, "she will play Camille."

The next day that post was destroyed by shell fire. And Katharine Hepburn lost a devoted fan.

Yes, it is much better in the movies. You are never disappointed in the movies. Or in the theatre. When people get killed they always come out afterwards and bow to you to show you that they are all right. It is too bad it doesn't happen that way in wars. If only all your dead friends could come out and bow after the wars were over, it would be fine.

The whole war in France was too much like the movies. You always felt you had been in the places before or had done the same things before. Except when you were very frightened or people were being killed you felt as if you were copying some movie actor. Hollywood did it all first. And they did it so completely that they didn't even leave you anything to tell your girl when you were both alone and frightened because you were such small people and your little love was being smashed in by the bombs and the 75's. Goddamn Leo the Lion.

The traffic was still snarled. The attack was still held up. You could hear some of your people talking to the ones coming down the other side of the road. They all said the same thing. It is hopeless. They are too strong. C'est perdu. C'est fini. Ils sont trop forts.

It made you sick to hear French soldiers talk that way. It was that glassy punchdrunkenness that made you sick.

Far off there was the hoot of a train whistle. Trains. How many had you ridden on during the last year. My God, how many!

There was that day going to the south to get your things, the war had just begun and you had just joined up and had three days to get your stuff. It had been very hot with the train fifteen hours late. Since morning the train had crept across the sun baked plain past mountains, hazy in the heat, past cracked plaster towns and dusty vineyards toward Marseilles. In the afternoon you were sitting on your rucksack in the center of a sweaty garlicky mass of people which had overflowed from the compartments and the corridors into the vestibule. You were hot and hungry and miserable. But you still held out one hope. At least, you thought, it cannot get any worse.

But you were wrong. It got worse at Arles where

another crowd of people came on. And it was then that the old man became wedged against you, half in your lap . . . half on your shoulder.

"Please pardon me," he said, "it is not my wish to so inconvenience you."

"That's all right. Don't mention it."

He shook his head. "It is always this way," he said. "Always when there is a war, it is the same. In '14 and in '70 I have had it the same."

"Really?"

"You see," he said by way of explanation, "I am of Strasbourg. This is the third time I have had to leave it because of a war. It is ridiculous."

"Where are you going?"

"To Marseilles. Some of my family are of Marseilles."

"Papa," a drab voice cut in. "Papa the gentleman is tired. Do not make him more so."

"My daughter-in-law." The old man said to introduce a tired sallow woman who had worked her way through the crowd. "My son has been mobilized. It is hard for us now."

"Yes," the woman added excitedly, "and I have had to leave everything behind. Everything. It is too much."

The old man chuckled. "She has a new cleaner

of the floor by suction," he said. "It is that she worries over."

"A what?"

"A cleaner of the floor by suction, monsieur. The newest and most efficient type."

"A vacuum cleaner," the woman said. "A Hoover vacuum cleaner. You have many of them in England, I believe."

"I'm American."

"Ah," her face lighted up. "Then you can tell me one thing I would like to know. Is the cleaner perhaps named after your late President Hoover? Does he perhaps make them?"

"He sells insurance, but he might have a sideline of vacuum cleaners, too. I'm not sure."

"It is a wonderful cleaner," she said. "Even a bit of a feather it will pick up. Even the head of a pin. It saves hours of labor and with it making the home is an easy thing to do."

The old man chuckled again. "It is all she does," he said. "Clean the floor. Day in and day out she is always cleaning the floor."

"And now I must leave it behind and the Germans will get it. Les Boches."

"The Germans will never get to Strasbourg," the old man told her.

"So you say," she sneered. "And what do you know of it?"

"Ask anyone," the old man became excited. "Look, I will ask."

He tapped a soldier on the shoulder. "Sir," he said solemnly, "would you be kind enough to give my daughter-in-law reassurances that the Germans will never reach Strasbourg."

"Of course they won't," the soldier said. "It is unpatriotic to think so."

"You hear," the old man told her. "You hear what the soldier says. It is unpatriotic even to think so."

"I am only thinking of my Hoover vacuum cleaner and various other household aids which I have left behind me in Strasbourg. I am not young and it hurts my back to sweep the floor."

"Madame," the soldier twisted about to face her. "It is idiotic to think that the Germans will ever reach Strasbourg. It is a stupidity to believe that they can get through the finest army in Europe plus the fleet of England which is the best of its kind."

The woman sniffed. "We see very little of the fleet of England at Strasbourg," she said.

"I speak of tactics," the soldier said angrily. "Tactically it is impossible for the Germans to ad-

vance westward. Madame, what of the Maginot
Line? Tactics, madame."

"What," she asked, "do soldiers of the second
class know of tactics? I speak only of my Hoover
vacuum cleaner. . . ."

"Ah, my God," said the old man, "I wish I had
never thought of it."

"You," she said. "You."

"All day long it goes hum hum. It is enough
to drive a man completely crazy. I hope the Germans do get it. I hope that when they reach Strasbourg . . ."

The soldier's face was stern. "The Germans will
not get to Strasbourg," he said. "They have nothing
of petrol or of coal. They have no things to eat.
No rubber tires. Or good autos."

"That's true," the old man said. "I have read
it in Paris Soir."

"And besides, madame," the soldier added sar-
castically, "I am sure they have a sufficiency of
Hoover vacuum cleaners which make keeping the
home an easy task. The Germans have always been
a mechanically-minded people."

"To their downfall, sir. To their downfall," the
old man added grandly.

The woman ignored them both. "You will
understand my concern," she said. "You are from

a country where such things matter. Perhaps your mother uses such a cleaner."

"I think she does."

The woman smiled. "The world is very small," she said. "Here we are, you and I, both owners of the Hoover vacuum cleaner. Tell me, does your mother have one of the sewing machines of Singer?"

"Yes. Yes, she certainly does."

"I, too," the woman answered proudly. "And has your mother, by chance, an electric refrigerator?"

"Yes."

"With a light on the inside?"

"I don't think so."

"The latest model," she said, "has a light on the inside. Perhaps your mother could exchange hers for one of the later models."

"I'll write and tell her so."

"Yes," she said. "Do that."

After Marseilles you and the soldier were alone in the corridor. The sun was down then. It was evening and cool air came through the windows. The soldier opened his musette and took a bottle of wine which he uncorked. He passed the bottle to you.

"And that," he said, "is all they care about. Vacuum cleaners. The dirty capitalists. It is for them we go to war. To get murdered. They'll get to Strasbourg all right. They'll get there. The Maginot Line was sold to them five years ago. It is common knowledge in the army. And," he said savagely, "I could be shot for saying so."

You did not answer. You were drinking wine.

The next night you sat at the table in front of the big café on the port in Saint Tropez. You were sitting there with Ian and his girl. It was night and there were no lights except the moon on the water and the little blurs of cigarette butts glowing from the decks of yachts in the port.

"Well," Ian said, "there's no doubt about it this time."

"No. No doubt this time."

"The last time they announced it on the wireless it was official. General mobilization."

Ian's girl shook her head slightly as if she might be trying to jar loose some unpleasant thought. She did not understand English, but she had understood those last two words all right.

"Might as well not talk of it in front of her," he said.

"Sure."

"Better not talk of it at all."

"I know."

"Do you think it will really come?"

"I don't think so."

"Impossible to imagine rather."

"I know."

"Have to leave early in the morning," he said.

"I know."

"Will you come along? It might take several days. We'll drive to Boulogne and then you can take the train back to Paris."

"I'll come."

"We'll go through the Burgundy. Eat and drink all the way. Give each other parties."

"Swell. Look, maybe I'd better go now. I'll see you after you've taken her home."

"That might be best," he agreed.

But when you stood up she pulled your coat for you to sit down again and she shook her head that you shouldn't leave.

"C'est mieux comme ça," she said.

"I wonder," Ian said, "will they take our kilts away. We've always worn them."

"They might."

"I don't know. We'd make an awful bloody stink at the war office."

"I'd like to see you in kilts."

"I have silver kilt pins," he said. "My grandfather left them to me."

"Did he?"

"You know," Ian went on, "we should really speak French. She can't get a word this way. Except, you know, I can't think of any French to speak. I only want to speak English tonight."

"I know," I said.

"We might get drunk after she leaves," he said.

"That's a good idea."

"I don't really feel like it, though."

"Neither do I."

"But suppose we ought to really. You never can tell."

"Maybe it won't come, Ian."

"Maybe not."

The phonograph started playing on the deck of a big American yacht out in front of us. The record they played was a jazz arrangement of the *Blue Bells of Scotland*. Some girl sang it. Her voice came crisp and clear from the yacht to where we were sitting.

"She sings very well," Ian said.

"Sure. She's good as hell."

"It's a nice song, too."

"It's a fine song."

Ian laughed. "I am glad the words are in English," he said.

"Me, too."

Ian's girl was listening to the song and watching Ian's face very carefully. She was a very beautiful girl and a very sad one.

"You know," Ian said, "I hope they don't have a lot of bloody songs this time. That would be frightful."

"I know."

"*Tipperary*," he said, "and things like that. No damned good, really. Make you feel like hell."

"*Keep the Home Fires Burning*. Christ!"

"Makes you feel a little sick and embarrassed when they do things like that. All the slackers know all the words."

"And the music."

Ian's girl leaned forward and asked what the song was about.

"C'est une chanson ecossaise," Ian told her. "Une chanson des fleurs. Elle se concerne avec les blue bells."

"Blue Bells?" she asked.

"Des petites fleurs bleues," Ian told her. "C'est une chanson des petites fleurs bleues."

"Oh." She nodded.

"We'd better go now," he said. "I'll see you after I take her home."

"Take your time. I can wait."

"No," he said. "There's no good in that."

They stood up and said good night. Then they

left arm in arm. You sat there listening to the music.

> Ach, the bagpipes should play o'er him
> And I'd lay me down and cry,
> But it's so in my heart
> That I think he will nae die.

Then it was over and a woman's voice on the deck of the yacht said wasn't it a lovely song. So earthy and simply. It almost made her want to cry. She did not explain why.

Afterwards in the bar drinking Ian looked over at you and said, "We really must get a little drunk."

"Somehow it seems hard as hell."

"I know. And we've had gallons really."

"Funny, isn't it?"

"Yes." Then he frowned. "You know," he said, "I wish they hadn't played that bloody blue bell song. You know?"

"I know."

You sat there for a long time after that and had many more drinks but still could not get drunk. It was very strange and puzzled you both for several days until one night in Macon, the night they finally declared war, you ascribed this physiological difficulty to the international situation.

And after that in Paris, sitting alone on a bench in the Luxembourg Gardens feeding the pigeons. It was the twilight of a rainy day. Night sopped down over the city like an unwashed corpse, blotting out the reds and yellows of the flowers, destroying space, leaving only sound.

You had been sitting there all afternoon. Whenever you had run out of corn for the pigeons you had bought some more. But now it was too dark and one by one the pigeons were leaving to roost. This frightened you. You didn't know why exactly but it emptied you as if when each pigeon left it took more than corn with it. As if when each pigeon left it took some little piece of whatever it is inside a man which makes him feel warm and brave and happy. Later you found out that this is Pernod, but you didn't know that then.

While it had still been light you hadn't thought much about being a soldier. Then you had just been a young man sitting on a bench in the park with nowhere to go on a rainy afternoon. But now you began to think about being a soldier again. Now you were conscious of your new uniform. It fitted you very well. Sometimes soldiers saluted you. This embarrassed you very much.

You were also conscious of a vague fear of death. Something which was more a yearning to be alive than a fear of dying.

It had all begun during the trip down to Paris. In the beginning this had been very gay. There you were in uniform and there were other men in the compartment. Strangers at first, but not for long. You remembered how each soldier in turn had brought a bottle out of his musette and passed it around until it was emptied and the next man brought out a new bottle. Red wine, white wine, calvados, and marc. It filled you with hazy warmth, dulled the nauseating part of your excitement and heightened the painful tingling element of it. Of course, there had been some unpleasant things, too. A little too much weeping. A little too much blaming of capitalism for their being in the army by the soldiers. It did not fit in with an army going to war and even then you were sure that there would be none of this sort of thing in Germany. Not that these men were anything but right, but men who cried in public were sick somewhere inside themselves.

Gradually the compartment had emptied. Stop by stop these weeping men had gotten off and you were left alone to look through the window at the sidings full of flat cars loaded down with the ugly shapes of guns under their canvas coverings. And the long empty hospital trains, their windows painted blue, a red cross on their olive-colored sides, and the occasional glimpse of the white antiseptic interiors. That's when fear had come. Alone in the dusty half-gloom of the compartment you had begun to think about yourself. All of it, the guns and stretchers seemed waiting for you. Your original idea of being part of a great army of men faded. You didn't want to be part of an army of men who cried in public. You were left with a feeling that you were the army. You were its heart and soul and body. All of its pain was in you and likewise all of its fear. You had never lost that feeling. You had an awful feeling of someday seeing these men run away. France never again seemed the safe brave place it had seemed before.

You got up from the bench. It was very dark now. You looked up at the sky. There was no moon. There was only a thick stretch of blackened cloud which blotted out the stars.

You went out to the street at the Place Rostand and hailed a taxi. You told the driver to take you to the Crillon.

The Crillon was full of noise and laughter and lights and women. There were many soldiers there, mostly British. Two people from your section were sitting at the bar. There was a girl between them. A girl with hair like a boy's cap, curling up at the ends.

When you went up and said hello it seemed as if
she'd never been away at all but she had been waiting for you there the whole time and had become a
little afraid that you weren't going to show up.

You ordered champagne and began to talk. Jok-
ing easy talk at first. Then the two people from the
section disappeared after two poules deluxes and
you were alone with her and then you began talking about other things.

You had a lot to drink and then you went to
Harry's and had more and to the Ritz and Meurice.
It seemed as if you never could drink enough or
talk enough together.

At one point in the evening you were sitting on
the terrasse at the Dôme. You watched the poules
pass up and down the Boulevard Montparnasse and
talked to her about the false excitement of such
things. You tried to tell her how the glamour of
such affairs, the real ones and the spurious ones, lay
in the mind of the man . . . not in that of the
woman. It is the poetry of young men themselves
which give women glamour. Women will never
know this, but it is true. You told her this sitting
on the terrasse at the Dôme where so many Americans had sat before you. You told her how sometimes there are women who have their own poetry,
not poetry exactly but a sort of musical background

to the poetry of the young men and that this sort of thing is love. And it is a marvelous thing and is mysterious and dark and very wonderful. It is two people sailing off on a tangent into the darkness.

You couldn't stop talking to her. And you both laughed to see all the fairy painters and phony poets nancying along the street carrying their gas masks. Some nuns passed. They too had gas masks, but this time it wasn't funny. You felt that this was a tremendous violation against God.

You wondered if the whores hung your gas mask up as carefully when you went home with them as they did your coat.

How you talked that night. Later you were with many people and were very drunk. But you were very happy because she was there, too. You weren't lonely any more and you weren't afraid and then you knew that your fear had been loneliness.

When you woke up in the morning you drew a cold breath and then another and the chill feathered down your belly until you thought the skin would break over your toes. You felt vague and loose. There was the taste of whiskey on the roof of your mouth, and when you raised your head the throbbing began, first lightly at the back of your skull, then spreading out and deepening in inten-

sity until the stabbing was tearing at your temples.
You sank back. You were hungry and cold. You
were filled with disgust. It was a complete hangover.

You closed your eyes again, wondering where
you were. You had seen your uniform hanging on
the back of a chair, but you knew you were not out
at the chateau with the section. The bed was too
soft. The pillow case was too clean. You tried to
remember step by step what had passed before you
had gone to bed. But you could only remember
fragments.

"Hello, are you awake?"

The voice was low pitched, but it cut through
the haze in your brain.

"Sure I'm awake."

"How do you feel, darling?"

Oh Christ, you thought to yourself, so it's darling, is it?

"I'm fine."

You turned your head in the direction the voice
had come from and saw the door to another bed-
room. The door was half ajar and you could see a
maid moving about inside.

"I'm sending a dressing gown in to you," the
voice said. "Come and have breakfast with me."

"That's swell," you said.

"You have a luncheon date at noon. At the Meurice."

"Have I?"

You shrugged your shoulders under the covers.
Jesus, you repeated to yourself, maybe I hired a
social secretary and she took me home with her.
While you waited for the maid to bring the dressing
gown you tried to remember what had happened.

You looked down the length of blanket to your
hands. They were very dirty. Automatically you
reached out to the bed table and fumbled until
you had found a match. You began to clean your
nails with it. The loose dirt came easily, but even
after you had finished your nails were still grey
with grease from the motors. You shook your head
sadly.

"Christ," you said.

"Don't," the voice said. "Don't please be pious
this early in the morning, darling."

Afterwards you went in and she was sitting up
looking very young and cool in a pale blue negli-
gee. Then you remembered and everything was all
right again.

It was that way all fall. There were so many
things that fall when your side thought they were
winning the war and you sat out in the Bois during

air raids and people went to Maxim's again just as they had during the last war and people sang *Tipperary* and *If You Were the Only Girl in the World* and you were all going to hang out your washing on the Siegfried Line.

Every morning there were the tanks going through Sèvres and when you woke up the hollows were white with mist and the ground was hard with frost which leaked coldly over everything, the trees and the windows and even the sides of the tanks. And you all went up to the Etoile one day and there were the Polish chasseurs and the French chasseurs and the Grenadier Guards and a long flourish on the trumpets and a tiny man with five general's stars laid a wreath and he was Gamelin, le sauveur des hommes . . . papa Gamelin and it was the eleventh of November. There were the binges out at the chateau. There was the time they fought with broken bottles and one of your people slashed up the adjutant and the adjutant's ear was hanging by a thread of skin and later that night the one who had done it went off wildly into the woods looking for a tree which would hold his weight. But he passed out before he found it. And there was the night three of you sat late in the mess crying bitterly because you could not get a platoon of beer bottles to do squads right. The mess was

a fine place. It was an old banquet hall made from
the stones of the original walls of Paris and there
was always a stretcher by the fireplace and every
night you had to carry somebody upstairs to bed in
the stretcher. They did the same thing at the Hotel
Moderne where the British stayed on leave and
there they always had a special detail of stretcher
bearers to dump the passed-out pilots into bed.
Every Saturday night there were parties at the mess
and everybody came out from Paris after the cafés
closed. Colonels and sergeants and whores and
duchesses, they all came and the duchesses ended
upstairs in the same bed as the whores ended up in,
only sooner. There were some mighty spirited
duchesses in Paris that fall.

It was a fine mess. And in the beginning there
were more servants than there were volunteers
And there the Ritz and Crillon and Meurice and
Suzy Solidor's and the Colysée and Ciro's and
Harry's and Harry never bought anyone a drink
and later all his ex-customers had a good laugh
when he was standing out in the road near Tours
begging for petrol during the evacuation of Paris.
There was Prunier's and the Plaza Athenée and the
Bœuf Sur Le Toit. There was Lucienne Boyer and
and there was Henri Bry. There was Chevalier
and Josephine Baker at the Casino. There was the

Duke of Windsor walking his dog mornings on the Boulevard Suchet dressed in his major's uniform. It was marvelous that fall when you thought you were winning the war and you all sang *Boomps A Daisy* and *Roll Out the Barrel*. Very few people had the bad taste to get killed that fall and it was very gay.

You used to sing every night after dinner at the mess. It was almost a high mass. You used to start off with *The Bells of Hell Go Ting a Ling a Ling for You but not for Me* and end up with *Stand by Your Glasses Steady This World Is a World Full of Lies* and everyone had chalked his name and dates on a stone in the wall so they could carve it there when he got killed.

II

My life is reft of laughter,
My clan gone down in slaughter,
Yet in some dim hereafter,
Is dawning of the day.

— OLD GAELIC AIR

YOU'D PLANNED A TERRIFIC CHRISTMAS. A FLAT IN Paris and a perpetual party going on for a week. But when Christmas Eve came you were on the *Norma,* one of two Finnish freighters crossing from Scotland to Norway. The clouds were low and heavy and the ship rocked badly because the wind was on her beam and the cargo of iron in her hold was badly packed. The ship was going through the mine fields. Nobody spoke much about this. But everybody thought about it all the time.

That afternoon a plane came out of the dark reefs of cloud and swung wide in lazy circles over the other ship, the *Virgo,* behind you. The Finnish serving girl came into the cabin to tell about the plane. She was very excited.

"*Flyg machine,*" she said in Swedish.

Up on deck the crew were all looking back over at the *Virgo*. At first you could not see the plane. You squinted hard until you saw a black spot swing out of a cloud bank. There were many gulls and at first it was hard to distinguish the plane from the gulls. Finally you were able to tell between them because the plane was bigger and its wings did not flap.

Then suddenly the *Virgo* changed her course and, without even a radioed message, she disappeared. This made the captain sure that the plane was German. The *Virgo* had been taken, he said, and German ships would be waiting to pick you up off the Norwegian coast.

You went down to finish your coffee. You weren't brave . . . it was only that you didn't believe the captain.

It was dark that night when the ship came up the Norwegian coast and dropped anchor. All around you was the black-humped coast line with many lights burning in windows on this Christmas Eve. The sky was cloudy but there was a thin bright band of blue night sky between the clouds and the tops of the hills. The moon shone mistily and there were the points of many stars. It was a fine feeling to be anchored in a harbor and not have to worry was your life belt ready on the top bunk and were all your most necessary clothes placed where you could get into them in a hurry. Suddenly you felt so very bursting good that, standing there looking at Norway, you began to bawl out Christmas carols. *Hark the Herald Angels Sing* and *Little Town of Bethlehem* and *Noel, Noel.* But these depressed you. They made you think of things left behind maybe forever. They made you think of superior letters from people at home all about the stupidity of being canon fodder. Such smug letters. As if all men in all armies were stupid. As if the armies were not full of young men who had girls and hopes and ambitions and dreams of beauty inside them. Your friends were cannon fodder and so these letters from home made you angry. Why should these safe people insult you with their pat little speeches? Nobody was asking them to do anything. You weren't asking any favors or asking anyone to feel sorry for you. To hell with them. That part of you was gone, you guessed. You were a soldier and the things of the army were in you. And if you ever did get home and tried to tell people this they would not understand it anyway. They would say you were trying to dramatize yourself when all you wanted to explain to them was that these young men in armies were not stupid and had lives and hopes and dreams the same as anyone else. It was

simple to you. But it was not so simple to the editors
of the magazines who made smart jokes about things
which were very important to you. Things like
bombing planes and your friends getting killed.
The war cuts a ditch between those who are in it
and those who are not. Those who are in it see
their task clearly and learn tolerance and sadness
and dignity. The others learn something else. It is
too bad. But it is true. And you are out of key with
them when you come home. The people who are
not in the war should realize that the young men
in it do not become unthinking beasts but only
learn to love the things they've left behind them
so much more than before that even thinking about
them is a wound.

You thought these things standing on the deck
looking at Norway and you pretended you were
saying these things to your friends at home and
sadly you knew that saying this would end all those
friendships and you would be lumped among those
they scorned as a person who had sold out to the
animals when all that really happened to you was
that away from newspapers and other people's
opinions, away from the latest plays and books and
cocktail parties and benefits for obscure people,
away from all these things when all you had in
their place were the words and actions of simple

men who were risking their lives, you had learned a new order of conduct. A simpler one and, to you, a more dignified one.

Hell, all you wanted was to live in a world you could look in the eye. It is in the Constitution of the United States what you wanted. But you also wanted to know that you had protected your right to this constitution, that you had paid your taxes for the benefits accrued. And for that they said you were playing soldier.

Down in the cabin the others were getting drunk and so did you. You were all quite drunk on aquavit at dinner and afterwards you made a tremendous bowl of eggnog and stood around the bowl singing *Auld Lang Syne*.

In the morning you woke up with a hangover and went up on deck to look at Norway in the daylight. The coast crumbled around the ship in great circles of grey rock and rusty pine with many bays and inlets and continual glimpses of rock and pine as far off as you could see in all directions.

On shore was a green church steeple, some shabby houses, and two camouflaged gasoline tanks. There were other gasoline tanks also. But they belonged to the Standard Oil Company and were painted bright silver. The camouflaged ones belonged to Norway which is a poor country and was taking no chances.

You had a terrific hangover and so Christmas morning was the same as if you had spent it in New York, Paris, London, or Niles, Michigan.

That afternoon you lay on your bunk reading and listening to the Belgian boy who had been a machine-gunner with Franco. He was Flemish, this boy, and a die-hard fascist. He was talking about Belgian politics and fascist tactics. He told about one Belgian deputy who went barefoot through the streets and slept through all the sessions of the chamber. This man had told the voters that a man should only work two months out of the year and he had polled a tremendous number of votes.

He was a nice boy. He had been wounded twice in Spain and now that he was reformed out of the Belgian army he was going to Finland to fight. The Finnish consul in Antwerp had given him a Sam Browne belt which he wore all of the time over his suit coat. He was terribly bloody-minded about the communists, but he loved to sing and sometimes he even sang the International. It was a song, he said, so why not sing it? In fact, he said it was a very good song. He was able to be completely detached about songs. That was because he loved to sing. Sometimes his singing annoyed the others and when he began singing they would say, "le music hall est en haut." That was if they were below. If they were top side they would say, "le music hall est en bas." Finally the Belgian boy took to lying in his bunk whenever he wanted to sing. You didn't get to be as good friends with him as you might have because he didn't drink like you did. You all drank too much and were quite gay, but he felt better than you did mornings. So all in all he probably gained much more than he lost.

The next day the boat had moved up the coast to Sweden and you got off at Malmö. The architecture of the town was fine, simple and dignified stone buildings with marvelous interiors. The inside of the police station at Malmö was very handsome and made much use of wood and steel and stone. From a window there you could look out and see children skiing around a Christmas tree in a little square.

You left Malmö by train for Stockholm early in the morning. It was pitch black except for the milky reflection of the snow. The train was good and it was very clean. Most of the passengers were Swedish peasant boys on their way to Finland.

The early morning sky in the country there was amazingly clear. It was a cold night blue, which softened gradually and thinned out until it was grey and heavy bellied with snow clouds. There was snow on the ground as far as the horizon and it clung in ropy drifts to the ugly red houses and red barns.

It was silver laced to the bare trees which fanned against the sky in sudden forests which rose swiftly from the plain like islands.

Riding along up through Sweden you remembered other train rides and other people you had met on trains. There had been the train trip from Bayonne to Carcassonne when the train had gone along the bottom of the bare brown mountains toward Pau and the fields at the side were full of people in blue clothes and sabots gathering brushwood. There had only been three of you in the compartment. The Austrian girl and her husband, the German baron, and yourself. And the three of you had gradually become acquainted and in some way had begun to talk of painting and writing. The baron was very fond of Beethoven and you discussed music and he asked had you ever been to Salzburg and when you said you had not he told you it was necessary that you go there some day.

Then he asked about art in America.

"You have any great painters?" he asked.

"We have one, Herr Baron."

"And he is?"

"His name is unimportant."

"And writers. I am very interested in writers."

"Yes, we have many fine writers. I think we have the finest writers in the world. I think some day the writing in America will be the greatest the world has ever seen."

"And the painting?"

"And the painting. And the music. And the architecture."

The baron had smiled. "An American renaissance?"

"Why not?"

He shrugged. "No reason at all," he said. "But first you must become conscious of your American soil. There can be no great art where there is no consciousness of the soil. No pride. Pride is important to a nation. At any cost a nation must have pride. At any cost," he repeated it.

"Even if it costs destruction."

"Yes." He bit the word off sharply. "Yes."

Suddenly you noticed that the baroness was extremely uncomfortable. It was in her eyes. She was frightened of something. You didn't know what it was.

"And," said the baron, "if this great culture does not come to America, what then?"

"Then I think there will be no more culture."

"Maybe not," he said. "But for all we know that may not hurt us one bit."

"I don't believe that."

"Who knows."

You were silent for a few moments. The mountains swept bare beside the track and far off high toward the peaks snow shone pink in the sunset.

Then he began to speak again. "I am a writer," he said.

"Yes."

"I am writing of the war."

"Please, Ernst." The baroness spoke and there was urgency in voice and there was fear in her eyes.

"We were betrayed," the baron said. "We won and then it was taken from us by your America. We would have had Paris had you not sent your fresh troops against us at Chateau Thierry. The English were beaten and so were the French. No matter what they say to you, America won the war for them," he said.

"Please," the baroness said. "Please, Ernst."

"For four years they starved us," he went on, "and still they could not beat us. We swept them away until they crawled and begged American help. America should have been our ally. Now it is too late."

As he spoke his face changed. His eyes emptied themselves of light and intelligence. "It was a crime," he said gutturally. "We would have swept them off the continent. We would have ruled in their place. We would have . . ."

He stood up. His whole body was tensed. He was sweating and his face had gone a purplish red.

"We would have . . ." His voice was thick and he kept opening and closing his mouth as if he were reaching for what he wanted to say. His hands twisted along the seams of his trousers.

Suddenly the baroness stood up and spoke again. "Achtung," she said sharply.

It was amazing. When she said it, he snapped to attention and stood stiff and silent as if he were on the drill field. And his face went pale.

You stood up and went out into the corridor. You did not look back. You looked out of the window at the mountains and the people gathering brushwood. The train stopped at Pau, where all the grey stone of the town spills down the side of the mountains to the track in layers of galleried streets.

It was a long time before she came out. When she did she touched your elbow softly.

"He sleeps now," she said.

"Won't you have a drink with me?" It was the only thing you could think of saying.

"Yes. I would like that."

On the way to the restaurant wagon you passed through the third class compartments. They were full of people who had come down from skiing in the mountains. The compartments were full of the smell of wet wool and wood and leather.

The two of you sat in the restaurant car and drank brandy. Whenever the train jolted some of the brandy would slosh out onto the table cloth.

"He has been that way since the war," she said. "You understand?"

"I understand."

"It was a bitter disappointment to him. In the beginning he could not eat or sleep or even talk. All day he only sat and hated. Now he is better. He must sleep with the light on, but he is gradually better now. We must keep traveling. It is good for his mind." She looked very tired and you could see she was much older than you had thought in the beginning.

Some young French boys came into the restaurant car. They were very gay and noisy and drank much red wine. They were dressed in skiing clothes.

"And now," she said watching them, "now it begins again. It is too much to ask of people. Too much . . ." She was crying softly to herself and trying to hide it by looking out of the window.

The French boys were singing *Aupres De Ma Blonde*. This was in the early spring of 1939.

That was the first time you had ever gone to Carcassonne. The next time you went there was on your leave just before you went to Finland. It was before you had even known you were going to go to Finland. And your girl was with you. You were on your way south for ten days' leave and you'd gone out of your way to stop at Carcassonne.

That night you went to bed in your room in the hotel which is built into the walls. The room was all grey wall paper and yellow satin drapes.

In the middle of the night you woke up. You felt scared suddenly and filled with premonitions. You could not get back to sleep. You thought about your friends and you were filled with sadness. Suddenly you saw behind all the fun and behind all the show you made wearing uniforms and saw only the sky by gun flashes and in that moment you had your first taste of unrelieved terror. It was something you hadn't even felt at the front.

So you put on your tunic over your pajamas and went down the hall to her room. You wanted to hear her laugh and say "Where are your guts, boy?" the way she always used to say it whenever you got fed up and spoke of quitting.

Inside her room it was dark and a soft wet wind came through the windows and her hair fanned out black against the pillow. You stood there a while and then she woke up while you were watching her, and you sat on the bed and talked and talked the way you had the first time you met her.

"We're going to get it," you kept telling her. "All of us. The whole gang of us are going to get it."

"No, darling."

"Don't tell me. I feel it," you said. "I feel very clean and pure and young. Like a young boxer before he goes into the ring or a very young bull-fighter. I'm way off somewhere out in space and nothing anyone does can touch me. And everything I've ever learned is wrong. They taught me all the wrong things."

"Maybe they're right, darling. And you're wrong."

"No fear of that. What do they know? My family for Christ's sake. What do they know about death? How the hell can you know about life without knowing about the other? If you're afraid of death you're a coward. If you deny it, you're a fool. What do they know?"

She laughed softly. "Darling, you love words so much. You love making a show of yourself."

"I know it. It's marvelous. I feel filled with myself to the brim. I feel sad and scared and brave and happy all at the same time. Right now I almost wish I was at the front again. I know so many things now. These others back home . . . these safe ones with the best bars and the best books and the best plays and their lousy little charities for England and France . . . what the hell do they know? This is the dark ages before the renaissance and I'll go through it and come back strong where they're weak."

"You're so damned young," she said, holding your hand and smiling up at you the way she had at the Crillon that day.

"So what? What the hell's being young? Waiting for things to happen. Now they've happened and I'm not young any more. I was brought up to know I'd have to fight in the next war. Well, this is the next war. Hell, maybe I'm old. What are definitions anyway? Maybe I'm old and you're old and so are Yehudi Menuhin and Shirley Temple and Bernard Shaw's an infant and that's why he has to eat vegetables. This is reality, you and I, and all the guys in the section. This is real. Every day you miss getting knocked out the present and the future by a breath. That's real."

"You're a bloodthirsty bloke," she said.

"We're fighters again," you went on. "And as

long as we fight for the purity in things we can still give out our music like Bach did and Shakespeare did. We're being washed clean again. We're . . ."

"Like us, darling? Like you and me."

"Sure."

"Are you still scared, darling?"

"A little," you said.

"Darling."

"Yes?"

"Let's leave now. It will be light soon. Let's leave so we can drive into the light."

So you left and drove as the light came and a soft rain was falling and, looking back, you could see the walls and towers of Carcassonne rising like cliffs up from the flat lands behind a soft shower of fine rain. And every once in a while you would look at each other and just smile and you stopped along the way and had croissants and coffee with rum in it and were pleased when the patron referred to you as "le lieutenant" and said "au revoir, Monsieur-Madame" when you left.

That was in Carcassonne and now you were in Sweden.

Sweden is being rich. Nothing more, nothing less. It is being rich as Fifth Avenue shopwindows are rich at Christmas time. It is snow sparkling along black water at night in the winter. It is the grey bulky sweeping stairwayed palace of the king. It is a milky dawn which lasts until noon. It is quiet-voiced well-fed business men eating salted almonds and drinking martinis at the Opera Bar in Stockholm. It is ships loaded with iron ore for anyone who can pay. It is not believing there is suffering and ideals anywhere. It is fatness and sleekness and drunken men sentimentally talking about Vikings. It is a few young men in white fur hats and white sheepskin coats fighting for Finland, betrayed by the comfortable people at home. It is a statue of Charles the Twelfth pointing a skinny warning finger toward Russia. It is the black Baltic and white plains. It is long nights and dusky cocktail-drinking afternoons. It is rich farmers. It is laziness and money love. It is being too fat to leave your chair. Sweden is being too rich for too long a time.

It was in Sweden where you met all the people who told you what a great and important thing it was for you to go off and help Finland. Then when you mentioned anything about Sweden doing the same thing they were shocked to death. And always they gave stupid college cheers for you and believed that by doing that they were helping Finland, too. But their king betrayed Finland publicly over the radio and let Russia know that Finland stood alone. And the Finns made a joke that the Swedes had had to get their king from France because there were no men in Sweden.

The Swedes felt sure that no matter what happened eventually to the whole of Europe, no war would come to Sweden. And they seemed to believe it was Finland's duty to save Sweden from Russia and that the Finns were lucky to have the chance for performing this glorious mission. And you felt that in spite of the intelligence of the Swedes and the beauty of the architecture and the fine manners of the people, Sweden was not worth saving from anything.

That was Sweden and you were glad when finally you were on board ship again sailing off into the Baltic toward Finland. And you were very frightened of mines and submarines and bombing planes. But finally at dawn one morning the ship ground through the ice and smacked the pier at Turku which the Swedes call Åbo. There were still many forebodings because on her last trip the ship had been bombed right at the pier. There were many holes ripped in the ship's iron work, many of the crew had souvenir pieces of jagged iron from the bombs and you thought, if this is what it can do to iron then what, for Jesus' sake, will it do to me?

There was Finland just over the side of the ship, the snow and the blue-grey sky and the windowless hulk of a bombed building. They hoisted the cars over the sides and you drove them down pitchblack streets with the shop fronts all boarded up, to a garage to have them re-camouflaged white.

The hotel in Turku was very nice and in the dining-room you heard more French and English than you had heard since you left France. There were many journalists and many Finnish officers who impressed you with their smartness.

You spent the short morning waiting for an air raid which didn't come and you left Turku that night for the front in charge of an English-speaking corporal.

Seven times you changed trains in the three days it took to make the trip. And gradually the trains became emptied of civilians. The last train was merely a caboose attached to a freight train. Your ambulances were on a flat car on that train looking long and white and ghostly with the dim outlines of the American flags painted to their sides shining faintly.

You drank coffee or tea laced with brandy in many station restaurants all of which were very clean and all of which were jammed with soldiers. You talked to one little boy of thirteen who was in a labor company and who had worked all the summer before on the Karelian fortifications. On one train you sat next to two soldiers who each wore the red and yellow ribbon of the Grand Cross. They had been in the hospital and now they were on their way back to the front. One of them had been out with a ski patrol twenty-four hours behind the Russian lines. It had been too dark up in the north for them to know where they were. They met a Russian patrol and shot them up and when finally they got back to their own lines this soldier found twenty bullet holes in his pack. And these soldiers told the story of the Finn in the hospital at Turku who had been left naked in a house by the Russians who had then set the house on fire. This Finn had escaped and had wandered naked in the zero weather and was now in the hospital. He only wanted to go back to the same sector and find the Russians who had done this to him. But this was unlikely because he had had both feet and an arm frozen off.

You slept wrapped in your coat on the train benches. Little spurts of light would drizzle down from the ceiling. The trip was long because the trains usually ran only at night.

For hours you sat watching the faces of the soldiers in this dirty light. The soldiers' faces were young-old and reminded you of the faces of Spanish soldiers you had seen at Hendaye in France a year

before. There were many women also on the trains
and they carried packs on their backs just like the
men and were going up to do men's work. The
soldiers taught you Finnish words and told you
army jokes. They told you how they called their
identification tags, "Cloches Molotoffs." And how
they called lice "Molotoffi."

The trip was tiresome. Sometimes you waited as
long as seven or eight hours in stations between
trains. Then finally you changed to a bus and rode
two hours through a snowy dawn with the sound of
firing faintly ahead of you. You went through
forests of jagged pine and passed lines of men in
white clothes skiing along the roads with their
packs humped under their snow suits, so that they
looked like hunchbacks, and their rifles slung stiff
against the sky. There were many sleighs pulled
by little horses and finally you stopped again and
a staff car picked you up and took you to the field
hospital.

That was all during Christmas week and it was
still during Christmas week when you and O'Hara
drove out one night, creeping without lights, driving so slowly, in fact, that sometimes it seemed to
you as if you were not moving at all.

You could hear the gunfire far off to the left and
if you looked across O'Hara's body, big and bulky

as it had looked at school, you could see the flashes against the sky, a continual lightning-like stabbing at the blackness. But it was far off and very remote.

It was the last night of the year and there were many things to think about. There was peace to think about. Lying on the beach near Saint Tropez with twisted little pine trees behind you and great pale stacks of dried seaweed and the sun baking into you and you and Joe were lying there and he was just back from Spain and having a pretty bad time. And you were both thinking about Elsie.

From the very beginning it had always been Joe and Elsie together. Everybody else fell in love with each other and out of love again a dozen times every summer, but not those two. They were always together. And when they were married everybody was at their wedding and then afterwards down at the boat to see them off and you and Joe had a couple down in the bar and he told you he was planning to stay over for a long time.

"Every time we have a scrap I don't want everybody knowing it," he had said.

"So what, Joesy?"

"I don't know exactly what," he said, "but just watching other people I know who are married around here gave me the idea. Christ, I know everything that happens to them. Everyone knows. I don't like it that way. You know?"

"Sure."

"And they all end up saying the same things and the same things are mostly dirty jokes. Not for me and Elsie. It's too good now. I don't want anything to spoil it."

"I know, Joesy."

"You come over after a while. We'll have some fun."

"O.K."

They traveled around for a while and then they took a flat in Paris up near the Etoile and Joe took some courses at the Sorbonne and they gave cocktail parties for people from home and people from the embassy and they bought a car and took long motor trips and in the winter skied at Kitzbuhel and Davos and learned to speak pretty good French. American French, but with the right inflections and idioms.

In general they led a fine happy expensive life and everything was fine until the Spanish war. Then Joe and Elsie got interested in the war and somebody talked Joe into investing a lot of money in a movie about Spain.

Joe made a couple of trips to Madrid and Barcelona and saw some of the fighting and then on one of his trips down there Elsie went with him and one

So you went down into the town and into the big
smoky café and Ian was there and Ian's girl and
with them was another girl with hair which curled
up at the ends like a boy's cap and eyes like cigarette
smoke. And that was the beginning of all that.

When you looked at her you felt from what you
saw that she had been waiting for you all the time
and had become a little afraid you wouldn't show
up.

You all went on a party that night and you talked
to her for hours and danced and when you were
dancing it was as if everything had stopped going
around except that here was this girl and she was
all you wanted out of everything in the world.

It was all hello, what are you like, what do you
think about, we'll have great fun, always fun, we'll
always be together, we're bigger than anything else
in the world. It was so simple that whenever you
looked at one another that night and for days afterwards you would both laugh out loud. Just because
it was so simple. Everything was wonderful. It was
like all the words to all the songs and all the movies
and all the sonnets plus boat rides and champagne
and langouste and sunshine and Monte Carlo and
Cannes and Antibes and it all started in a big smoky
café in the south of France on the same day that
the Italians moved into Albania.

It almost ended right after the war started. It almost ended when you were sitting in that café again and you were back for a weekend after joining up. And you were sitting at one small table writing a letter and she sat at the other watching people come through the door. When the people interested her she would squint after them until they had seated themselves and ordered whatever it was they wanted.

"Most of them order coffee," she said. "And after that Cinzano is the favorite."

You grunted and went on with your letter.

"And," she said, "it is the second Sunday of the war. The war began last Sunday. And the Sunday before that was still before the war when we waited for it but didn't think it would really come. That was our great English optimism which does the whole world so much good."

"What?" you looked up.

"I'm giving you the news," she said. "It is the second Sunday of the next world war and most of them take coffee although Cinzano is a strong runner-up."

"Oh."

"Now you may go on with your letter. Your life and letters. Who was the American who wrote his life and letters? The one who helped get you into the last war?"

"Page?"

"That's it," she said. Then she laughed. "Oh, Page," she said, "thou shouldst be living at this hour. England has need of thee. Not really, though. We don't need anyone this time."

"I know." You bent over your letter again.

"The lights are going out all over Europe," she said, "and we shall not see them lit again in our time."

"What?"

"That's what Edward Grey said."

"Oh."

"Darling."

"Yes."

"That isn't true. Is it? They're not going out. Not for good." She sounded a little scared.

"I don't know."

"Please no, darling."

"I don't know," you repeated it.

"They mustn't," she said. "It mustn't be that way. There simply has to be an afterwards, darling."

"It doesn't matter."

"But it does, darling. It does," she said. "It matters to us. Can't you see that? This is just the beginning of something awful. I know. I know what people did during the last war. Darling, we can't just have that."

"I can't tell you anything."

"All right, darling," she sighed. "Go on with your letter."

And so you went on with your letter, trying to kill off the whole thing because you were afraid of just what she had talked about. You were afraid of what it would turn out to be and what you would involve yourselves in. You didn't want to hurt anyone and you knew you would if you went on. Even now leaving after a few hours' permission to go back to the army filled you with a crazy sort of desperation and you knew it would only become more so and more so, especially once you got to the front. If you ever came back then, you knew it would be too late and somebody would get hurt. It was better to kill it before that happened.

"Is it an important letter, darling?"

You shrugged.

"Anyone I know?"

You shrugged again.

"All right, darling, I won't pry."

"Thanks. You're marvelous that way."

"Thank *you*, darling."

After all, you were writing, if it can't be forever

like other people's then let's quit at the beginning.
It won't hurt so much now. But let's not get caught.
Let's not let everything go to hell and us a part of
it. At least not in that way. Not you, anyway. I
won't even tell you what you are now. That's getting caught. Why start something they won't let
us finish? It was fun that first night to play falling
in love or to fall in love or to make eyes at each
other or whatever you want to call it, but we
shouldn't have done it. Let's just write off the last
four months, you wrote.

"Are you almost through?" she asked.

"Yes, almost."

"Is it a nice letter? Is it full of nice wise sane
American thoughts."

"I don't know. I haven't any nice wise sane
thoughts. My thoughts are all old and wearing
pretty thin."

"Don't be modest, darling," she said. "I love your
thoughts. They're so nice and shiny."

"So are my blue trousers, but they aren't new
either."

We picked the wrong time, you were writing.
The wrong time and the wrong place and you probably picked the wrong person. That's all.

"Darling, do you think they'll have more gas
masks next week?"

"I guess so."

"They have lovely ones at the American embassy. They cost four guineas but they really are good ones. An officer I know told me that they're the best ones in the country. America takes awfully good care of you."

"Sure."

"Well, I hope they do have more. I feel so conspicuous without one. I think they might have waited before they declared war to see if they had enough gas masks to go around. That sounds silly, but it isn't really when you think of it. What if they haven't enough guns to go around? It isn't so silly when you think of it that way, darling."

"I know."

Her voice changed and she looked serious. Whenever she looked serious she also looked very young.

"I don't think I'll be afraid in air raids," she said. "I was a tiny bit afraid in the first alerte, but that's because I was all alone and I had to go down in a cellar with some old women. One of them was a Czech. Do you know what she said?"

"What did she say?"

"She said, 'I'm a Czechoslovakian. I don't care what happens to me!'"

"The cheerful type."

"Well, you can't really blame her, darling. But

I do think she needn't have simply shrieked it so.
The rest of us weren't Czechs and we jolly well
cared what happened to us. But she actually
gloated, darling. I mean, I think if we were Czechs
too, it would have been all right. But it's such a
naked thing to say. I hate people who say naked
things like that. It's so embarrassing."

"The French don't say them."

"Yes, they do, darling, but they say them in a
way that rather puts clothes on the whole thing."

"A lot of your people say them."

"I know. I met a boy the other day who kept
calling them 'Jerry' and 'Huns'! Really, darling.
Why can't people just call them Germans?"

"Pretty bad."

"Was it not, darling?"

You signed the letter and sealed the envelope.

"Do you mind if I get rid of this?" You asked.

"Of course not, darling."

You stood up and walked swiftly to the door.
When you got there, you tapped the maître d'hôtel
on the shoulder.

"Look, will you give this to the young lady?"

"Yes, monsieur." But he raised his eyes as if he
were afraid you might be playing some joke on
him.

And you didn't see her again until that evening

at the Crillon and when you saw her then you knew
that you didn't want to kill it off. Not for one little
minute.

And now it was the last night of the year and
you were sitting with O'Hara in the ambulance and
the snow stretched limitless on all sides and far off
there was the gunfire and the flashes tearing away
the darkness on the line of the horizon.

"What time is it?" O'Hara asked.

You looked at your watch. "A couple of minutes
yet. You sure we won't get into trouble?"

O'Hara nodded toward the back of the ambulance. "He can wait," he said. "It won't kill him."
Then he laughed. But it wasn't funny, the point of
the joke being that the man was already dead. He'd
died three kilometers back. There'd been a gur-
gling noise back there and you'd switched the light
on to see what was wrong and you'd seen that the
man was dead.

"Well, now we don't have to wait until we get
back to the hospital," O'Hara said. "We can be
traditional now."

You turned to look out at the road again. There
was no moon that night. And you could barely see
the black lines of the trees at the side of the road.
You turned up the collar of your coat. The fur
rubbed softly against your ears.

"This is the first fur coat I ever had," you said.

"Everything comes to him who waits," O'Hara grunted. "I'm stopping. It must be just about time."

"Just about." You looked at your watch again.

He shifted into neutral and pulled up at the side of the road. He throttled the motor down and let it idle. The sound was barely audible in the stillness which flowed out to break up only against the distant pounding of the artillery.

"They're throwing a lot of stuff tonight," you said.

"The Swedes are over there."

"I guess that's it. Poor bastards."

"They won't hit anything. They're trying to scare them out." O'Hara fumbled with his hand in the rack over the windshield.

"Got it?"

"Yeah," he said. "Here it is." He brought his hand down. You could see the glint of the foil around the bottle's neck.

"Baby," he said and made a smacking noise with his lips. Then he began trying to force the cork out of the neck of the bottle.

"I wouldn't mind whiskey, tonight," you said.

"Me, too. It was silly lugging this damned stuff along."

"Whiskey and peppermint. Irish whiskey and peppermint would be great tonight."

"It's fine against the damp," he said.

"How long did you live in Ireland?" you asked him.

"About six years."

"Where?"

"Dublin mostly. Merrion Square."

"Just like the Duke of Wellington," you said.

"And Oscar Wilde," he added.

"Dear Oscar."

"We'll drink to him," O'Hara said, "if I can ever open this bugger of a bottle."

"Stuck?"

"Yes. And the damned thing's colder than hell."

"Ever do much fishing in Ireland?" you asked him.

"Sure. Near Killarney."

"Brown trout?"

"Yeah. When were you in Ireland?"

"About a year ago. I was going to go there this January. I'd have had ten days' leave then. I was going to go there with a girl. The fishing season opens the end of January, I think."

"I don't think it opens until February," O'Hara said.

"Maybe not."

"You wouldn't have gotten there anyway," he said. "It would have been hard as hell getting to England even."

"Not with a carte militaire."

"Yeah. But it wouldn't have held for the Free State."

"Maybe not."

"Goddamn this bottle." He was still wrenching at the cork.

"It's almost time."

"I can't help it." He tugged at the cork.

"Let me try."

"All right." He handed you the bottle.

"I can't help thinking about that guy back there."

"Well, don't. We can't do anything now," O'Hara said.

"Yeah, but it seems so damned bloody-minded to worry about this bottle with him there."

"Is he covered up?" O'Hara wanted to know.

"Sure."

O'Hara started twisting around to get at the back of the car.

"Where are you going?"

"I want to see something."

He opened the door on his side and got out. You could hear his feet crunch over the packed snow then you heard him open the back of the ambulance and get in. He was gone a few minutes. Then he came back.

"How you coming?"

"No good. I think it's frozen."

"All of it?"

"Yeah."

"Let me see." He took the bottle and smacked it against the side of the car a couple times, the bottle broke off like a piece of wood. The champagne was frozen solid. "For Christ's sake," O'Hara said, "we should have had whiskey."

"Lucky us. Let's go."

"O.K.," O'Hara said. "Happy New Year."

"Happy New Year."

He started the car bumpily and you moved off down the road.

"He's awfully young," O'Hara said nodding toward the back of the car where the dead soldier was.

"Yeah, I know."

"I closed his eyes," O'Hara said. "I thought that would be better."

"That's fine."

You looked out of the window back toward the yellow line of gun flashes. The gunfire was spreading out now. It was more general along this entire front. It was behind you now not only to the left and it was louder and by the time you had to drive back on your next trip you would be in it.

"Some New Year's Eve," O'Hara said to no one in particular. "Some New Year's Eve, I don't think."

It was the last night of the year. You often wondered why it was that so much of your life seemed to have happened that night. There was the night the Russian moaned, for instance. You were a full ambulance load coming back from the front that night. It was during the cold spell when the temperature went down to fifty-seven degrees below zero Fahrenheit and you were mostly frozen cases. Your feet were frozen. You'd frozen them that afternoon. You'd been up there on one of the trips you made to get captured medical supplies. You were walking down the road with a medical captain and you'd both been struck by the fact that among these captured supplies were many bottles of blood for transfusions which would now be used to keep Finnish soldiers alive instead of Russian soldiers. This was a subject for philosophical discussion, but you had not been able to enjoy any such form of archaic amusement because the shelling was pretty heavy and most of the time you were either headfirst in the snow or lying on your faces in the road. It was very cold. If you breathed for a few minutes with your mouth open it made your throat so sore you could hardly swallow. It was a painful cold. It knifed into you and twisted in you like a cramp. Especially where it hit your feet.

Then suddenly your feet stopped hurting. Warmth flooded through them and a numbness set in and you knew they were frozen. When you got back to the medical tent you took your shoes off. That was very hard to do because you could not bend your toes. The doctor watched anxiously as you did this because many times when men had frozen their feet badly they would remove their shoes and leave some of their toes behind inside their shoes. Finally though you got your shoes off and you found that the inside walls of them were covered with that fuzzy frost which you see coating the parts of refrigerators. These shoes were French skiing boots which you had gotten in a little shop just off the Boulevard des Capucines. They were heavily greased and were fine for such places as Saint Moritz or Chamonix, but not for Finland, where it was so cold that the grease froze and turned your shoes into a pair of ice boxes.

Your feet were white and hard. The skin crackled sharply across them when you walked and your toes clinked almost like ice cubes in a highball glass. The medical people rubbed them alternately in snow and in hot water. Then the toes turned blue as they began to thaw and the medical people put iodine on them and bandaged them and shoved you into the first ambulance back to the field hospital.

The ambulances were big single-deck buses and in them the stretchers were slung on hooks from ropes in the ceiling. Some of the ambulances still had the regular seats and could carry many sitting cases. It was very crowded and smoky in the ambulance that night, but this made it warmer than it would have been otherwise so nobody minded the discomfort. Everyone was drowsy from the cold anyway and wanted only to sleep.

You sat in the aisle between the bottom row of stretchers, sitting with your back propped against the stretcher on one side of the aisle and your feet braced against the opposite stretcher. In the stretcher on your side was a Finnish sergeant whose leg had been broken by machine-gun bullets. Opposite you where your feet were was a wounded Russian.

The Finnish sergeant passed you a cigarette and in the light from the match you could see his face pale with the shock of his pain and strained with the struggle to keep silent about it. That was one of the things you noticed about the Finns, the only times you ever heard them cry out was when they were unconscious.

"You are English?" he asked me. "I have been in England. I was a sailor."

"No, I'm an American."

"Ah hah, that is very good. There are many of you?"

"No. Not many. Very few."

"But you are good fighters. All Americans are good fighters."

"I'm an ambulance driver."

"You will be fighting yet," he said. "In the end there will be no more ambulance drivers. We will all fight."

"Probably."

"You won't mind that?" he asked.

"I don't think so. Maybe, but I doubt it."

"It is very easy to get used to," he said. "You get so that you do not want to stop. And, besides, we must each of us kill fifty Russians."

"I know."

"I have killed already twenty-seven," he said. "Ten of them at one time yesterday with a Russian automatic rifle. It is very good, the Russian automatic rifle."

He showed you how he had been lying in a hole
dug into the middle of a road and how there had
been this semicircle of Russians around him and
how he had wormed his way backwards toward his
own lines while he had kept firing with the rifle until he had killed all ten of them. He showed you
where two of the bullets had gone through his cap.
Three had landed in his thigh.

"It must be very painful," you said.

"It is all right."

"They will give you morphine at the hospital."

He smiled faintly. "That will be very good," he
said, "but I can wait."

After that you fell asleep. The ambulance jolted
along over the ruts and skidded around turns.
Every once in a while it would hit a particularly big
rut and that would wake you up and you would half
open your eyes and see the lines of stretchers, swaying slightly, and hear the heavy frosty-breathed
breathing of the men and smell the heavy odor of
blood and antiseptics and tobacco and sweat and
finally you would drift back to sleep. You knew the
road fairly well and could tell from the turns that
you still had a long way to go.

Then one time when you woke up you heard
the Finnish sergeant swearing.

"Percole," he said viciously. "Percole satana Molotoff." This was the worst curse in the Finnish language.

"What's wrong?" you asked him. "Does your leg bother you? Is there something I can do for you?"

"No," he said, "it isn't that. Listen." He pointed toward the Russian.

The Russian was moaning. He tossed about on his stretcher and moaned.

"Listen to that pig," the Finnish sergeant said. "Listen to that cowardly dirty pig."

"He's in pain," you said.

"Oh no," the Finn said. "He is hurt very slightly. They told me that. Only hurt in the flesh. He is a sitting case, but tied down on the stretcher to keep him quiet. They are all crazy with fear, these pigs. These communist hogs. These Molotoff bastards. Keep quiet," he yelled at the man in Russian.

"You speak Russian?"

"I am from Karelia."

"I see."

"Shut your mouth," he yelled at the man, first in Russian, then in Finnish, and finally in English to clinch the whole affair.

But the Russian kept on with his moaning and men all over the ambulance began to wake up and swear at the Russian.

"We do not do this in Finland," the sergeant yelled at the Russian. The other men in the ambulance were beginning to yell now. In the stretcher above the Russian was a Finn who was wounded in the head. He raised himself on one arm and looked down at the Russian. "Maybe you wish now you had stayed at home," he said. "Maybe you would live longer."

The Finnish sergeant nudged me. "That man is crazy. He will kill the Russian. He kills every Russian he sees. They burned his home and his wife died of exposure. He will kill the Russian. See. . . ."

I looked up. The man in the top stretcher was leaning over now. The effort had started the wound in his head to bleeding again. But he had a pistol in his hand.

"We do not cry when we are hurt in Finland," he said.

The other men had quieted down now. They left the affair to the man with the gun.

"Hadn't we better stop him?" you said.

"Stop him," the Finnish sergeant said. "Why?"

"It is only fair."

"Fair. So we ask them to make war. They make war and come here and we kill them. Does it matter how we do it or when we do it? If we don't kill them they take our country and make us slaves. Fair? Percole!"

He was so right, there was no point in talking any further. You knew he was right. In your heart or your stomach or wherever you feel the truth you knew the sergeant was right. It did not matter how you killed them. If they were after your home, you had to kill them to keep it.

"Now once and for all will you stop the racket?" the man on the stretcher said. "Otherwise I kill you. See, I give you a chance. Once and for all."

The sergeant translated this for the Russian who only kept on moaning.

The other men in the ambulance watched silently.

"We don't do that in Finland," the man with the gun suddenly screamed at the wounded Russian. "My wife did not do that." And then simultaneously with the end of his sentence there was the crack of the revolver and a puff of the smell of spent powder and the Russian jerked once and was silent with a hole through the center of his forehead.

There was a long silence. The ambulance skidded to a stop. The relief driver came back quickly. He stood over the Russian and flashed a light on him.

"Who did this?" he said.

"It was suicide," a voice said. "All Russians commit suicide. They are morbid. They do not die like other people. It was suicide."

"Who did this?" the driver stormed. You could see the one stripe of a corporal on his shoulder.

Again there was silence.

"Once more I ask who did this?" the driver said.

"It was . . ."

"Yes, yes," the driver said. "It was suicide. He is tied down and he committed suicide. Once more I ask . . ."

"Corporal," a quiet voice spoke up behind you.

The corporal turned quickly and went toward the voice. When he got to that stretcher and flashed his light his manner changed. He stood to attention stooping slightly under the low roof. "Yes, sir," he said. "Yes, lieutenant."

"It was suicide," the voice said in the same quiet tone. "Now let us start. It is very cold."

"Yes, lieutenant."

The driver went back to his seat and the ambulance started again.

After a while the Finnish sergeant spoke. "Perhaps I wouldn't have done it," he said. "Or you wouldn't. But now we will sleep anyway. That Russian made too much noise." He turned his head and was silent.

You sat there and you became drowsy again.

There wasn't even the smell of powder any more to remind you what had happened. The lieutenant behind you was silent, gasping slightly in his sleep with pain.

That was one of the things which had happened at night. And there were many others. And you were sure you had learned more at night than you had in the daytime. Thought better and more clearly at night. Many nights you had thought about writing, nights when it seemed you would probably never write again. That's when you really learned something about it. That's when you saw that it had to be and that you had to go through with it, twisting it and shaping it and making it a truth as simple and clean as a child saying its prayers or a tree dropping its leaves. That's when you finally saw behind the articles and speeches made by men who talked about being professional and about writing being a business. It was those nights when you were quite sure you would never write again that you realized that these men had dwelt so long in that weariness they called success that they were no longer proud to be writers and tellers of stories. They wanted to be something else, bankers or salesmen, just as the popes of the Renaissance wanted to be generals and kings instead of priests. And you wished you could make a speech in front of a bunch of young writers. Not writers in their twenties or thirties, they're already old writers. No, you wanted to make a speech to little boys and girls in the sixth grade who were sitting down to write about their favorite pet or their favorite holiday. Those were the young writers. And you wanted to tell them that if they set down what they had to say as simply and honestly and cleanly as possible and if they were right inside it would come out the way it should and there were really no words to describe this cleanness that writing should have, but that it is in everything you do. It is the way you live. There is no word to name it. Some people call it art and some people call it God and those are as good words as any. But all good art has it. There is a thin clean line which links it all up . . . Beethoven and Bach and Rembrandt and Cézanne and Shakespeare and Ring Lardner, they are all linked by this one simple cleanliness. The Finnish people had it in their way of living and, perhaps, that is why you thought about it so much in that country.

You learned about it from the Finns and from other single people, too. You learned much of it from a girl with hair that curled up at the ends like a boy's cap. A girl who used Chanel and wore grey flannel slacks by Creed and loved escargots and said darling in eighteen syllables. And when you began to learn it from her you were so frightened because she was so right and you were so wrong and had been wrong for so long that you did not see where you fitted in the whole scheme and you tried to run away from her. Only now you saw that as much as anything you were not running away from her but from something else because it shone out in a pale glowworm light that made you feel ashamed of yourself and of easy clever things you'd thought and said and done. And of an easy clever life you'd thought you'd made for yourself and people had patted you on the back and you'd gone on this way. Until first you met this girl and saw something so totally first rate and wonderful that it made you sick just as a kick in the stomach does. And then you learned more from the Finnish people and from dirty tired soldiers in Finland and in France. From simple people who, in spite of all the talk and slogans which decorated their sorrow with gaudy bunting, were dying where they didn't want to die, were going through what they didn't want to go through, were denying themselves everything that was safe and easy because some decency, some pride inside themselves had been invaded and they were fighting to keep it intact.

You learned a lot about it from Einar's sister, Astrid. You went to the Ivonens' for a three-day

permission. They lived in a big house on an island, on the same island as the Ivonens' factory.
Across the river from the island, was a big town
where most of the Finnish munitions were made.
The river was frozen over and the part of the town
near the bank was all frame houses looking dingy
with their covering of greyish snow.

The house was very big and the architecture
was good. It was furnished very simply and had
fine hardwood floors. There were many windows
at the back of the house looking out toward the
hills and the forests away from the town. There
were many hills in that part of Finland. There
was better skiing there than the other parts of the
country and the people who lived in that section
considered themselves the best skiers in the country. Einar had told you that. He had told you
many things about his family. He enjoyed talking
about them. His mother was Swedish and she had
great difficulty talking Finnish and she spoke it
with a thick accent. And his father was one of the
great Finnish industrialists. He was also a great
sportsman and the walls of the house were covered
with pictures of hunting dogs and birds and fishing scenes. He and Einar spent the greater part of
the spring and summer shooting and fishing together and in the fall and winter his father went

skiing every day after his work was through. Einar's father had been one of the organizers of the
Finnish revolution in 1918 and had been a captain
of cavalry under Mannerheim.

You had arrived at the house very late one night
when all the family was in bed except Einar's
father who had sat up waiting for you. As you
came up the path carrying your pack he stood
straight and tall in the doorway and welcomed you
with only a handshake, but made you feel that
you were at home before you had even entered the
house.

You were very shy in the house. Shy about sitting down because you were so dirty and because
you had lice. But Einar's father seemed to know
all that and he showed you to your room and then
made you a great stiff whiskey and all the time
you were filled with an almost hysterical sort of
joy because of the soft lights and the nice furniture
and the rugs and the whiskey, the sort of thing
you had not seen for weeks on end.

After you had finished the whiskey you felt better and sat down and talked with Einar's father.
It seemed you had never felt more at ease with
anyone in your life. Maybe it was because you
knew so much about him from Einar and because
they looked so much alike. Maybe it was the

whiskey. But probably it was Ivonen himself who
made you feel that he was as proud of you as Einar's friend as he was of his own son. You talked
and talked about the front and about Einar and
gradually he got you talking about America and
your own life there and you told him how you
wanted to change that life when the war was over
and make it simpler. How you wanted after the
war was over only to do your work and have everything very simple and be where people didn't try
always to say things to hurt other people. You had
more drinks with him and talked all about yourself. You told him how unimportant all the people
you'd thought counted seemed to you now and
that all they were to you now was a bunch of pale
faces sitting around cafés or in the lobbies of thea-
tres talking about stale things with stale clichés.
You told him how unnecessary people like the
ones whose names were famous in New York
seemed when you compared them to the soldiers
you knew or to the peasants you saw. And now
you guessed you'd learned that there were a lot of
things better than having everyone speak nicely
about short stories you'd written and funny things
you'd said. You even told him how you were afraid
to go home when the war was over, if you were
still around, because you knew you were going to

tell these people what you thought of them.

"I think that would be very imprudent," he said, smiling. "And also very smug, which is much worse."

"I guess you're right. But they're so tired, those people. They've spun their dreams out and they're at the end of them. All they can do now is crawl around spitting in streets. They're dead."

"Yes," he said, still smiling, "but these people are the ones who are going to decide whether your books are a success or not, you know. They're your immediate critics. It is perfectly good to feel the way you feel, but don't tell them about it."

"It's only honest," you said.

He shrugged. "What you will write should be honest. You don't have to say it twice."

"Yes. But it seems hypocritical."

"You don't have to see them," he said. "To be with them and insult them is no different from being with them and agreeing with them. Don't be afraid of hypocrisy. Do you think Voltaire didn't have complete contempt for the people he saw every day? Or Swift? Or Flaubert? Or Turgenev? Of course, they had. And," he said, "don't make the mistake of thinking that what you are doing is too important. You only set down what you see. Think of the importance of those who do what you set down. Don't belittle them."

"I'd like to stay here in Finland."

"No you wouldn't," he said. "Come back here. Come back again and again. Come whenever you feel you need whatever it is we've been able to give you. But stay where the language is your language and the earth is your earth and let the writing always have that language and that earth as its backbone. Go wherever you want. The more the better. But always have a home. And have that home in your own country among your own people. What you love about Finland and about France is that the people for the most part stay there. They don't ramble all over the globe. Remember that."

You nodded and he went on.

"France, for example," he said, "Russians, Americans, Swedes, Germans, Spaniards all go to France to paint and to write, but the Frenchmen don't go to other places. It is absurd to say that these foreigners could not have done their work at home. And these other countries have not had the clear unbroken line of fine work that France has had. The tradition of French painting, painted on French soil. French writing, written in France about France, and for France. The French artist's main concern has always been France. The Frenchman is no internationalist. He has been confused as such merely because what he has wanted for France has been good for other places, too. But the Frenchman does not think of the other places. They are unimportant to him. The English are not insular, it is the French who are."

" 'God is a Frenchman,' " you said.

"Yes. That's it as far as the French are concerned."

The front door opened and a girl came in. She wore the khaki ski pants and khaki trench coat of the Lotta Svard.

Ivonen rose. "And this," he said, "is Astrid."

You shook hands with her and then suddenly she started to laugh and pointed to your cuff. "Molotoffi," she said.

You looked down and saw a small louse crawling on your sleeve. You were completely shy and embarrassed again.

"Astrid," Ivonen said reproachfully, but he was trying hard not to laugh.

Then you laughed, too, and killed the louse when you thought they weren't looking.

After that you saw Astrid all the time. You went about with each other and told each other many things and asked each other many things.

She told you how terrified she always was in the air raid watch tower. And hours after her turn of

duty was over she would still hear the bombs echo-
ing in her head and, worse than that, the ugly chat-
ter of the machine-guns which came when the
planes would dive over the tower. Three girls
had already been killed at the job. She told you
how sure she was she was already dead when the
machine-gunning happened because she could not
understand how anything could remain alive under it. She told you all this and you knew exactly
how she felt. She had been there when one of the
girls was killed and she said she would never forget the shocked, almost surprised gasp this girl had
given as she crumpled to the floor of the tower and
lay there crookedly, her arms flung over her head,
her face palely looking skyward, her legs bent, and
that stream of blood glistening black in the moon-
light. Astrid had only been able to shrink against
the railing and shiver as she watched the girl die.

It was a girl Astrid had always known. She
could remember her in a hundred ways. It was like
looking through a photograph album of the girl's
life. Astrid could see her at every age. As a little
girl, then as a girl of fourteen or fifteen, and finally
as a young lady. And now she could also see her
as a huddled, bent, bleeding figure staring up im-
personally at the men who had killed her.

She told you how she would think of girls in

other places, in other countries. In America, for instance. They were so safe with their pretty clothes and their parties and their sweethearts. They went to bed at night and woke up in the morning and could go to school or university or stay home or buy things. The main thing was that they were safe. Safe. Safe. Safe. The word drummed in her head until she began to hate these girls for having this safety.

She kept saying to herself that work she had to do was not for girls. But she knew it was. It had to be. They could not spare the men for it. It was her country, she told herself, that mattered. But still she envied these girls listening to syrupy smooth dance music, going to the movies, going for automobile rides, going places for tea and cocktails, doing hundreds of things which were happy and warm. She thought of all the people who had been killed and she wondered would it go on until everyone was dead. That's the way the men spoke. To the last man. That's what her father said and she knew he meant it. Maybe, she thought, it was the end of the world. All there was now was for her to do her duty. It was funny, she thought about how all her life you'd heard words like that and never thought about what they meant and suddenly you saw that it meant lying dead in the cold. That was your duty. Well, she knew she still believed in it, even if she was frightened and unhappy she believed in it and she said that maybe it was by sticking to these things that you were able really to appreciate and love the other things you wanted so badly. There were worse things, she said, than getting killed. Letting your own sense of personal dignity down was worse.

And you talked with her about your girl. And she asked many questions about her and you tried to answer them, but it was hard. There were so many things you hadn't time to discover. You'd laughed and joked and left so many things unsaid that now, alone, you wondered about them. You told Astrid how hard it had been to get over your embarrassment about dancing with your girl. The moment you'd known you were in love with her, you were afraid to touch her. You were afraid to do anything that might turn out to be silly. So you were purposely silly all the time. Everything had been the same as the dancing part. There were hundreds of things you'd thought about saying to her, but they were never said. Sometimes when you were waiting for her in some bar or other you'd fill up with a strange burning feeling in your chest and you felt that the minute she came in you wanted to pour it all out of you in hundreds of words. You could almost see them shining like stars. But when she would show up it was impossible to say them. And still she knew you were in love with her and you knew she was in love with you. You wondered if people who really did love each other were ever able to say those things. Astrid said she didn't think so. They thought them and that made them act in a certain way, but they never said them. And you said that probably when it was all over you would have people say those things in books you wrote and wasn't that an awful thought? To go pawing over these things that had once been so shiny and new and clean, and you said it was too bad you could not stop the people who meant something to you from reading what you wrote. Only, actually inside yourself, sometimes you wanted them to read those things because it was the only place you were able to say them. You were able to tell Astrid lots of little things about this girl. You told her, just as you had told Einar, all the things this girl liked and what you thought she looked like and Astrid listened because she knew it pleased you to say these things. It was easy to talk about them to Astrid and Einar because they would never see the girl probably. And you told Astrid how once you had been in love with a girl and you had written a whole novel just to tell her the way you felt about her and then when the girl had read the manuscript she had criticized it in literary clichés and you had gotten mad and torn it up and had never seen the girl again. And Astrid listened and laughed with you about it.

That was Astrid. And she was killed on March 12, 1940, when she was nineteen years old. She was killed on duty at the watch tower the day before the war was over. And she was buried where the tower stood along with the other three girls who were killed there. Einar was buried at Viborg which is now Russian territory. And there's only you left out of the three and many times you think it was a pretty poor exchange. You hoped some day you would go back to Ivonens', but always you felt pretty certain that this was only another one of the things you kept telling yourself you'd do, but would never actually do. Once in France you burned a candle for Astrid in the church at Domremy. You guessed it was a pretty silly sentimental thing to do burning a candle for this Finnish girl in the church of Jeanne d'Arc, but you guessed maybe they would both understand. Anyway, by that time you'd gotten to be a pretty silly sentimental person, which is one of the things the war did to you. At least while it was going on. After it was over the sentimental part began to seem like wasted motion. But during the war it had been very satisfactory. Self-dramatization and sentimentality are two very necessary narcotics in war time. At least they were for you. It was better to see yourself as something out of one of the more attractive of the Farewell to Arms books than as a dirty, bleary-eyed drunk who was very likely going to get his head blown off.

Bravery is one of the most interesting things about war. And the most interesting thing about bravery is the discovery that it is controlled fear. When you were in school one of the staples in your required reading for Lower Middle English was an essay by Stevenson on the subject of bravery called Aes Triplex which means triple in brass or some such dark figure of speech for courage. In this essay there is an account of people who live their lives on the side of a volcano and who after each eruption go back, rebuild their homes, and live on. This, the Lower Middler is told, is bravery. This is not bravery. This is stupidity, as are most of the other things which the world, or at least that section of the world which spends its time collecting shining examples, confuses with bravery. There can be no bravery where there is no fear. What is particularly brave about a man

who faces a danger he does not recognize as such?
But a man who is terrified, as are ninety per cent
of soldiers in the moment of battle, and who still
goes ahead, as do ninety per cent of soldiers in the
moment of battle, is brave as are ninety per cent of
soldiers in the moment of battle. Bravery is made
up of stubbornness, pride, and a sense of duty.
These are the things which keep armies from becoming hysterical masses of men. This, of course,
happens. And it is not a pretty sight to see. But it
happens infrequently in ratio to the times it does
not happen. Much has been said by parlor strate-
gists about the cowardice of the French soldier
throughout what has been called the Bataille de
la France. This is completely unfair. Yes, the
French soldiers ran, and so did the Polish soldiers,
and so did the Belgian soldiers, and so did the
British soldiers. But only when there was nothing
else to do. Only when intelligence made it star-
tlingly clear that there was nothing left to face but
slaughter which would have been stupid. These
parlor critics of military affairs do not mention
and probably do not know that these French soldiers had been foodless for weeks, sleepless for
weeks, ammunitionless, leaderless, and were punch
drunk from incessant bombing, and had, before
they retreated, undergone losses which will make

the world's hair stand on end when the truth is known.

Bravery is a silent thing. It is dignity. It is the sort of thing which it breaks your heart to watch. It is the sort of thing once seen is never forgotten and you're a better person for having seen it. It gets in your hair and in your eyes and in your ears. It spoils your good meals and even a cigarette when you remember it. The memory of it spreads over everything like the dust off manure and many times it stops you from sleeping. It is God. It is music. It is the human race. It is bravery. Aes Triplex.

You discussed this one night in Finland with a soldier. A ski patrol of ten men, nine men and a boy really, came in late one afternoon. They'd been lost for two weeks in the snow behind the Russian lines, and had had to fight their way home. The boy was wounded. His arm was broken by a bullet which hit him just above the elbow. He was about seventeen and had straight blond hair which hung in bangs over his forehead and a little snub nose. He was very dirty and his clothes were soaked by the melting snow and frost. You helped him take his coat off and then his tunic and then several flannel shirts. You had to cut off the top to his woolen underwear because you could see you were hurting him even though he made no noise. While you were doing this one of the nurses told him to let down his trousers. He blushed and shook his head, he looked questioning at you.

"It is for the anti-tetanus shot," you said. "It is necessary."

"But . . ." He was terribly embarrassed. The nurse was very young and very pretty. She was about the same age he was. She might even have been a year younger.

"Look," you said to the nurse, "I can give him the shot. Last night I gave many such shots."

She hesitated. Then she saw the boy's embarrassment and nodded that you should do it.

You took the boy's trousers down and swabbed the place where you would make the injection and then gave the injection as quickly and as professionally as possible. When you finished you looked up and saw the captain-doctor looking at you. He was grinning his approval.

"Interne, driver, soldier . . . these Americans they can do everything," he said to the boy. "This one even has learned our language. Except for the verbs," he added.

The boy was very shy. "I would like to see America," he said.

"Would you?" you said, leading him to a chair

and having him sit there while two soldiers wheeled in the Roentgen machine.

"I have read of it in school," he said. "It must be wonderful."

The soldiers set up the machine and then the captain-doctor came over and looked at the boy's arm through the lens box which he held in his hand on a stick. The lens box looked like an old stereoptican machine.

"You stopped a good one," he said to the boy.

The boy ducked his head shyly.

"Does it hurt?" the doctor said.

"No, captain-doctor."

"He's a little liar," the doctor said to you in English. "I like such little liars. It breaks your heart." He looked very carefully at the arm. "Very well," he said. "The Norwegian can take this one." He sent a nurse for the Norwegian doctor.

You wished that he would do the probing for the bullet himself. The Norwegian was a good doctor, but new to this work and the best doctor in the world still has to learn to probe for bullets quickly and easily and without weakening the patient through pain. You would get very fine doctors there of many nationalities and in the beginning they all had the same fault. They were not used to working after bullets, which is a tricky technique and they

were unused to working over people who had not
been anesthetized as completely as possible. Therefore unwittingly they caused the wounded much
unnecessary pain. In surgery it is better if a doctor
has a strong imagination and can in some way
realize the pain he causes the wounded. The Finnish doctors had this. It was all personal to them.
Every case was, and there was one word they repeated at short intervals all through the probing
and the work when the wounded man was not
under an anesthetic. "Tuska?" they would say,
"Tuska?" Meaning "Does it hurt?" It was always
as if the soldier's father or his older brother were
taking care of him.

When the boy was on the table, the Norwegian
came in and the captain-doctor told him where the
bullet was and then the Norwegian looked through
the Roentgen machine and then got ready to go
to work. You stood by the boy's head, holding it
lightly between your two hands.

The Norwegian began cutting away flesh the
first thing and as he did the boy's face went green-
ish white and great drops of sweat appeared on his
forehead. He shut his eyes and clamped his jaw
tightly.

Finally the Norwegian began to probe. Deeper
and deeper. He was a little nervous and he took an

interminable time over it. The surgical nurse's face
took on a disgusted look. And this, of course, made
the doctor even more nervous. He did not understand Finnish and she kept making remarks to me
in that language.

"He is a butcher," she said. "Even you could
take that bullet out. He is a fumbler."

The boy's face was squeezed tight. You tightened
your hands about his head.

"It will be all over soon," you said to him in
Finnish. "Soon now."

"It is all right," he grunted.

The Norwegian's probe scraped over the bone.
There was a spasm of nausea which contracted the
boy's stomach muscles. You reached behind you
quickly and placed a small dish next to the boy's
face. "Here," you said, "if you would like to be
sick."

The boy opened his eyes and stared at you. He
gritted his teeth and then with an effort he opened
his mouth. You thought he would be sick, but
instead he stuck his tongue out at you and then
snapped his mouth shut and again gripped his jaw
muscles tightly.

Finally the Norwegian got the bullet out. He
passed it to you in a dish and began bandaging the
wound. He did not clean it out too much. They

had learned that it would heal better if it were not too assiduously cleaned.

"Lentecona," the nurse said to me. That meant airplane and was a frame made of wire splints which held the arm in such fractures so that there was no drag on the muscles and so that the broken pieces of bone would knit correctly. They had taught you how to make such splints, and when they had, one of the doctors had drawn you a diagram showing you exactly what it did.

While they were fixing the splint you suddenly noticed that a soldier was standing next to you. He was very dirty and looked completely worn out. He was one of the men of the ski patrol.

"How does it go, Veikko?" he asked the boy.

The boy opened his eyes. "All right," he said to the man. Then, "This is an American," he said nodding toward me.

"Yes? I am a Karelian," the man said. "Where in America are you from?"

You told him and he nodded gravely.

"You have come here all the way from America?"

"I have come here from France."

"Ah," he smiled. "We Karelians are called the French of Finland. We are gay and love music."

At the mention of the Karelian Isthmus the boy

smiled proudly. "I am from there, too," he said.

"We have fine music in Karelia," the man said. Then he looked down at the boy. "Did they give you the bullet, Veikko? You must have them give you the bullet. It always is so in such cases."

"It is here," you said. You washed the bullet off in alcohol and gave it to the boy. He was sitting up now as they bandaged his arm onto the lente-cona.

"It is very small," the boy said looking the bullet over disappointedly.

Finally they finished and the captain-doctor told you to take the boy to a bed. He did not want the boy moved that night. He wanted him to have some sleep.

Outside the surgery were the rest of the men of the ski patrol. They were very anxious about the boy and when he appeared they all grouped around him to see how he was. He proudly showed them his bandaged arm and they patted him on the back as if he were a pet of theirs.

"Take good care of him," they said to me. "He is a very fine boy."

You got him to bed and then sat with him a while after he was there. He was very disgusted about being wounded, especially when you told him that tomorrow you would drive him to the war hospital where he would stay for a couple of weeks or more.

"Now I am no good any more," he said. "I cannot help any more."

"You've done enough," you told him. "You're very brave."

"No," he said. "I am not brave. The others are brave. My God, you should know how brave they are. I couldn't even tell you."

"You're all right, too."

"No. I am not brave. I am just ordinary. But the others are. It is an honor for me to have been with them. They are fine. They are the finest men I have ever known. It was an honor." For a moment he looked as if he would cry. "I am not brave," he repeated, "but," he added, "I am not a coward. I know that now. It would be impossible to be a coward with those men."

The codeine you had given him began to take effect and his voice went drowsy.

"No," he said sleepily, "I am not brave. But I am all right. I can do my work without being a coward." He yawned. "It is a great satisfaction for a man to know that he is not a coward," he said.

Then he drifted off to sleep and you went away wishing that you had that same satisfaction.

When you got back to the main room the men

of ski patrol were waiting for you. They had collected some money. About fifty marks. You guessed they had pooled all their money for this amount. It was for the boy. They told you to give it to him in the morning. He could buy white bread and chocolate and cigarettes with it.

"He is very brave," one of them said. "Just having him with us was enough to bring us back. We couldn't have let down with that boy there. You have no idea how brave he is."

The doctors were all marvelous people. At least the ones you came in contact with were. There was the young doctor who froze his hands. You met him when you'd first come to Finland and the night you'd first really noticed anything about him was during an offensive when the hospital was crowded to overflowing. There were wounded on every inch of floor space and the surgical staff had been at work for fifty-odd hours without a break.

You were in the surgery working with this young doctor, picking up behind him and seeing that the lights over his operating table were constantly refilled with kerosene and doing other odd jobs such as wiping blood off the floor after an operation and scrubbing blood off the oilcloth covering of the table and fetching hot water.

It was well past midnight. The man on the table

had a shattered skull and the doctor was removing
the pieces. It is hard to tell just who knew first that
the man was dying. It may have been you. You
were standing at the foot of the table, holding
tightly to the man's ankles so that he could not
kick. Or it might have been the nurse who knew
first. She was at his head, standing off to one side as
the lieutenant worked. She had given the soldier
a lot of ether. Time after time she had saturated
the inside of the mask and then replaced it over
the soldier's face. Now she was afraid to give him
any more ether. She might have sensed it first that
the soldier was dying. Any number of people might
have. Except the lieutenant. He was too busy picking pieces of the soldier's skull out of a round hole
in the soldier's head. He did this with a pair of
pincers, laying each removed piece of bone carefully on a cloth. Sometimes the pincers clicked
against the jagged edges of the man's broken head
or scraped over the bone inside of the aperture.
When that happened you could see vicarious pain
mirrored in the nurse's eyes and she probably saw
the same thing in your eyes.

Anyway you were certainly one of the first to
know what was happening to the man because you
were concentrating very hard. Sometimes you used
to think of other things while you were working

there. You would think how much like a book or an etching it all was, the dirty broken soldiers with snow-soaked clothes wetting the table and blood crusty faces staring up at you. And you would think about the way the wounded smelled. You could not place that smell. It was an odor peculiar to the sick and the wounded. Once some friends of yours were sick and when you went into their room in the hospital, even they smelled that way. That had been a great surprise to you and you had questioned them carefully about it, but they could not help you out. You had decided that it might have had something to do with their diet. Later you decided it was the odor of blood mostly. It hung over the whole hospital like a smoke pall. It was like the lice. You got it from contact with the wounded.

But it was bad for you to think off in tangents like that because it made you careless like the time you were holding the foot of a man with a broken femur while the doctor bandaged the leg into a boot-shaped cardboard splint. You were supposed to hold the man's foot in a certain position and keep a steady straight pull on it. You began thinking about abstract things during this and several times the surgical nurse had to correct you or they would have bandaged the man's foot in such a way

that it would have healed crookedly and he would
have limped all his life afterwards. Since that time
you concentrated very hard on what you were
doing. And so you caught it the minute the soldier's leg muscles relaxed and the nurse looked to
the doctor and shook her head at him that it was
useless for him to go on picking bits of bone out of
the man's head.

The doctor straightened up. He looked very
tired. His arms were bloody to the elbow and bits
of brain and blood clotted skin stuck to his rubber
gloves. He looked down at his hands and flexed
them. Then he sighed heavily. This was the fifth
case he had lost in twenty-four hours.

After the doctor walked away from the table to
make out his report you set the dead man to rights
as best you could so that they could ship what was
left of him back to his family. The nurse bandaged
up his head. You helped her, folding the man's
hands and re-dressing him. You then noticed that
on one of his blue black grimy fingers he wore a
wedding ring. You had to try hard not to imagine
what his wife looked like.

Later you went outside into the kitchen for a
cup of tea and the doctor was sitting there looking
down at his hands. He was twisting his own wedding ring around on his finger and when you came

in he motioned for you to sit down with him.
He spoke no English and at the time you spoke
very little Finnish. He pointed to his hands and
shivered, making the motions of extreme cold.
And you remembered the story they had told you
about him. He had come to the front straight from
medical school. In the beginning he had been a
battalion medical officer working at an advanced
first aid post up in the north and he had frozen
his hands working in the intense cold, because he
had worn rubber gloves. You nodded as he explained, making quick short skillful gestures, the
kind a surgeon makes with a scalpel. He made
these gestures and then made a grimace of disgust
to show you that he knew that whatever it was that
had made his hands superior and capable of carrying out his technique had gone from them in the
cold that night up at Petsamo when he had frozen
his hands because he had worn rubber gloves. He
hadn't needed them doing this ordinary first aid
work, but they were a kind of badge of his profes-
sion and he had worn them. Without them he
would probably not have injured himself.

Suddenly as he was illustrating this for you he
clenched his fists and spat at his hands and jammed
them very quickly into his pockets as if he were
ashamed of them. Then he got up and walked out

of the kitchen, leaving his tea untasted behind
him.

Then one night while he was assisting the major
on a belly wound, the major found out about his
hands. The operation was almost over except for
sewing up the incision. The major and the lieutenant were pouring distilled water into the hole
in the patient's belly and then were putting their
hands deep into the hole to slosh the water out
again, when suddenly the major, who had been
watching the lieutenant very closely throughout
the operation, grabbed the lieutenant's fingers and
squeezed them very hard. He was able to tell immediately that the lieutenant had no feeling in the
tips of his fingers. The major shook his head sadly
and the lieutenant shrugged. He had expected this
all along and now that it had happened he was re-
lieved it was over. After that they transferred him
some place farther back of the line and gave him
administrative work to do in a base hospital. You
didn't hear of him for several weeks and then you
heard that he had gotten himself transferred to the
artillery.

Then one night they brought him in with his
left arm blown off and half the shoulder with it.
You all went in to talk to him. He was conscious
and very glad to be back. They gave him a private

room, the only one there was and he lived there for three days after which he died. While he was there a party of American newspapermen visited the hospital and you told them about him and then when they wrote their stories your mother sent you one of the articles from America and all it said was how tears had rolled down your cheeks because of the young surgeon whose arm was blown off. It was a very maudlin story. You had not cried over him. Nobody had, you just stored up what had happened to him along with other things which had happened to other people and which rolled together made a lump of hate inside you which helped you go on without sleep or anything, working toward the destruction of this filthy thing which had come into Finland and made all this needless sorrow. The lump of hate is still there. It's one of the things which keeps you from ducking out and hiding alone some place and saying to hell with everything. Some day maybe your hate and all the other lumps like it will be more than hopeless rage. And a man can walk with his girl in the park and there will be no shadows on the springtime and every hello won't be the immediate preface to an eternal goodbye. Someday there will be these things and the people of the world, the little ones and the big ones, will walk heads up again. Only first these lumps of hate must stand together at another Suomussalmi and then perhaps there will be an end to murder and a beginning of peace.

It is all unrest. All of it. The whole business of living. Love, hate, ideals, and ambition. Love is the best of them all. And love is the most of this unrest. There is a serenity in hating. There is even a quiet in the midst of war when fury whirls in circles around you and you, untouched, rest calm.

But love is being involved in someone else and being mixed into their hates and prides, and without it the whole of the rest is dull and does not shine. There are too many goodbyes. It seemed to you after a while that there were more goodbyes than hellos and that made for a sort of sadness. Love is very sad, most of the time. But it is something you want. In the war you wanted it more than anything in the world. Nights and days and hours and minutes you thought about it. You thought about girls, all girls. You were in love with them all. Your own particular girl and all the rest. You thought about them and talked about them and were terribly in love. There is no peace in thoughts like that. There is no peace in being in love. It is torment and misery and all the more sad because at the back of it is goodbye. When you fall in love you forget this, or, you stave it off with dreaming and then it comes and you're left a little emptier than before. It's all memories and touches and sounds and sharp feelings inside yourself.

You went on and on falling in love over and over again and sometimes you wondered where it would all end. Every time you held somebody's hand or kissed somebody or had your own private jokes with them you wondered how it would all end. You wondered did people just go on until there was nothing of them left except what remained in other peoples' memories. Even while you were in love with one girl you could still be in love with others. How were you to know which one you wanted for all things forever? Sometimes it made you a little desperate. You went on looking at everyone you saw and you did not know what you were looking for.

And at the back of it all was a girl with hair like a boy's cap curling up at the ends. There was something of her in all the others. She was there all the time and made it a little better than it would have been without her there.

And at the end when she was gone and you knew you probably wouldn't ever see her again there were other girls and you were better with

them than you would have been if she had never
been there at all. She gave something of her to
those others, too.

She knew that. She'd said it many times. She
said one night after you'd been dining with O'Hara
and some other people from the section. They'd
gone off to Montmartre and you'd stayed away and
walked with her. It was a fine night. You'd walked
away from the restaurant out into the Boulevard
Saint Michel and then along the river. The water
was black and the stone walls and steps down to
the river looked very white and clear and the trees
bent low toward the water and great dark loops of
moss snaked along the stone. The lamps along
the river pasted long oily golden tracks on the
water and up the river Notre Dame squatted over
Paris.

She had been very serious that night. Her face
was blurred and hazy in the dark and her mouth
was deep and soft and turned down at the corners.

"Why didn't you go with them?" she said.

"I wanted to be with you."

"You always want to be with me."

"I know it."

"That's wrong."

"It might have been wrong before the war,"
you said. "It isn't now. Not when you don't know

what's going to happen."

"It's still wrong," she said. "I don't want you to be with me all the time."

"I'm in love with you," you said.

"I'm in love with you, too, but it's silly of me."

"No, it isn't."

"Yes, it is. You'll go away, or something will happen to you and then I'll wish we'd never been in love."

"I'll never wish that."

"Yes, you will," she said. "You'll feel it after me, if it's you who's left."

"It won't be me who's left," you said. "I can tell you that."

For once she didn't get angry when you talked about that sort of thing. "Then it will be me," she said. "Do you think I want that? Do you think that's fun? Aren't things rotten enough without something like that happening?"

"I don't know."

"And what am I if you're gone?" she said. "I'm just a silly girl who did a lot of things that were jolly foolish. You know what they call it?" she said.

"That's only in bad books," you said. "Books by old gentlemen who've become recently impotent or ladies who've had change of life."

"Don't try and make it something clever," she

said. "It isn't clever. It's serious. We're a pair of fools."

You stood there, looking over the embankment at the river. You looked down at her. She looked very young and straight and clean. You put your arm around her but she shivered and moved away.

"Do you think I had to fall in love with you?" she said. "I let myself do it. And I wish I hadn't. If I met you now for the first time, I wouldn't let myself. I'd strangle you off in my mind. It would be easy."

"That's because you love me," you said.

"Of course it is," she said. "I wouldn't have to do it, if I didn't. Don't keep fishing so, I'm not going to say it again. Not ever."

"All right. Then I'll go. That's what you want me to do. Isn't it?"

"Yes," she said in a small muffled voice. "That's what I want you to do. Then it will be fine. I'll go home and go to bed and in the morning Rosalie will bring my coffee and croissant and people will come for lunch and I'll go to meetings for the Red Cross and it will be fine."

"Oh yes," you said, "it will be simply swell."

There was a terrible feeling of your stomach dropping away through your shoes and of everything going hard and cold.

"Oh," she said, "I don't doubt that I'll be sad in the beginning. I'll feel just as if I'd been to the theatre to see Hamlet and Maurice Evans is dead. And you feel a little sad and empty inside until you go somewhere and have a drink and start laughing again."

"Or maybe John Gielgud," you said.

"No," she said. "Not John Gielgud. I couldn't feel that way about him."

"You might even wear black," you told her.

"Oh don't joke about it," she said. "Just go. Please go. Please, please, please."

Suddenly you felt terribly angry and hurt and surprised. You saluted her very stiffly and correctly and turned away and then just when you'd gone a few feet you heard her give a choked sort of little gasp and turned back and went to her and the next minute you were holding her very closely and she was holding you. You were holding her so tightly that all your arm muscles hurt. And you turned her face up to you and her eyes went very wide and something snapped like a skyrocket inside of you and you felt almost as if you wanted to cry and then you were kissing her very hard, coolly, on the mouth, and you were both hanging on to each other as tightly as you could.

From then on you both tried hard never to be

serious because there was this sense of goodbye at the back of it that you'd brought out into the open. And so you clowned all the time with each other and said everything with an elaborate sense of mockery because you were afraid and embarrassed to be serious about yourselves ever again.

There is too much goodbye in the world. Every minute has its own goodbye. The whole thing is one long goodbye. There was a girl on the train to Helsinki who knew that. It was after the war was over and you were on your way home. All Finland was refugees then. There were five hundred thousand of them out of four million people and this girl was one of them. You were sitting on one side of her and an infantry colonel was sitting on the other in the railroad compartment. She was dressed in country fashion. A shabby wool skirt, two pairs of woolen socks, skiing shoes, and a beret on her head. She was not a very pretty girl, but her skin was good and her eyes were clear. She had cracked chapped hands. Big hands with long fingers and gold rings pierced through her ear lobes. She wore double gold wedding rings on her finger.

She was very unused to riding on a railroad and looked out of the window excitedly. Then feeling she had to speak to someone she turned to the colonel.

"I have never seen all the country before."

The colonel was a kind-voiced tired old man. "What is your district?"

She told him where she came from. It was near Latokka. It was now part of Russia.

"We are farming people," she told him. "Only now we must go to Helsinki. The government will buy our cattle. They have said so."

"They will," the colonel told her.

"He drives the cattle," she said pointing to her rings. "We will meet in Helsinki."

"Is he driving the cattle all the way?" you asked her.

"Yes," she said. "He and his brother and my brother. It is very hard."

It was terrific. They had to drive this cattle, walking themselves, all the way across Finland in the melting spring snow. Mile after mile, through the forest, across the hills and across the plains along the slippery slush-choked roads.

The colonel shook his head wearily. "There are so many," he said.

"We will work," the girl said proudly, as if he had implied they would be a burden on the country.

"Of course you will," the colonel said, "but it will not be easy."

"It was not easy before," the girl told him. "Farming is not easy."

"I know," the colonel said.

"Nothing is easy now," she told him. "It is not easy for anyone. Not for the Marshal even."

"It is less easy for the Marshal than for us," the colonel said.

"They have no one like him back there." She nodded in the general direction of Russia. "It is enough that we have someone like him. We will be all right."

The colonel nodded.

The girl sat there and ran her finger time and time again over her rings. Her face was sad and apprehensive. She turned to you.

"It will be safe now, won't it? Traveling the roads."

"Yes. Safe, but very slow. The roads are full."

"Yes," she persisted. "But there will be no dangers will there?"

"No," you told her. "No dangers."

"They will not come back with the airplanes?"

"No."

"They used to come every day with those," she said.

"I know."

"One day there were two hundred of them, one

after the other, leaving little lines of white smoke until the whole sky was criss-crossed."

"Condensation from the exhaust pipe," the colonel said.

"I don't know," she said, "but it was really very pretty."

The colonel shook his head.

"What is your district?" she asked him.

"Ostro-Bothnia," he told her.

"It is flat there, isn't it?"

"Yes."

"They have not taken any of that, though."

"No, it is still ours," he said.

"Where were you?" she asked you.

You told her.

"And they have taken that, too," she sighed. "They have taken so much. Why did they take so much?"

"They need it for their defenses, they said," the colonel answered.

"What harm could we have done them?" she asked.

The colonel shrugged. "It is an international affair," he said bitterly.

"They have taken so much." She repeated it. "So many forests and farms. Such old farms," she said. "Such pretty farms." She turned to you again.

"Our farm was very pretty in the springtime and the summer," she said. "So pretty that it made me sad when the fall came. I would think that maybe this time the snow would not melt and I would never see the green again. I would pray that the spring would come again and the lakes would shine with little waves and the trees would have back their leaves. A farm is very pretty in the springtime," she said.

"I know," you said.

"Now it is all gone to them," she said. "Why did they have to take so many farms? Such little farms. Why?"

"Those farms are of great international importance," the colonel said, bitterly as before.

"I have two children," the girl said to you.

"Yes?"

"Yes," she said. "Very small children. They have been sent to Sweden. Someone there takes care of them. I don't even know the name. Now maybe I will have them back."

"Of course you will."

"Maybe," she said. "Now he is off on the roads with the cattle and they are in Sweden and I must go to Helsinki."

"You will all be together again soon."

"Maybe," she said. "Maybe."

She turned her head to look out of the window again. "They shouldn't have let them take the farms," she said. "Not the little ones."

And the cobbler knew about goodbye. In peace time he was a cobbler and in the war he was a sleigh driver. One of the men who carried the flat wood boxes of ammunition up to the line at night and carried wounded back to the second dressing station. You saw men like him on the roads at night and could tell whether there was an attack through them. When there was an attack the roads were full of these lines of flat horse-sleighs piled high with boxes of bullets. They came onto the main roads out of trails in the woods and you caught them up suddenly in the blue white beam of your head lights, these sleighs slipping up high on the curves, the driver standing at the reins, cursing and shouting and saying prayers to the horses and the sleighs swinging into your car and you having to stop while they shoved the horses out of the way and untangled the sleighs when they bumped together and you would stick your head out of the car and yell.

"Get those bloody sleds the hell off the road. Must the wounded freeze to death because you cannot handle a horse?"

And you would see them come into the warmth

of a room or a tent at night, blue-faced from the
cold, their collars and scarves and mustaches and
eyebrows white with the ice from their frozen
breath like the rigging of a Gloucester fisherman
in the winter time.

And the cobbler was one of those. In peace time
he had made shoes and harnesses for his village
and even during the war he kept his box of tools
and bits of leather with him and he lived in the
same hut as you only in the next room and day-
times, while the others in his room drank coffee
and played cards and cursed the Russian planes, he
worked with his cobbler's tools. He made you a
holster for your pistol and while he shaped the raw
new leather and stitched it you watched him and
he told you all sorts of things about his village and
about the shoes he made there.

He kept the box of his tools in the bath-house
when he wasn't using them. And he told you all
these stories of the shoes he made for his village.
But what he really told you was that the greatest
thing in the world was for a man to have tools and
raw leather to work with and hands that could
shape it. What he really told you was that when a
man had these things he could say damn-all to
everything else and live in quiet pride because his
tools were sharp and his material was good and his

hands were skillful. And he cursed the Russians as those who had taken away this certainty and robbed him of the dignity of his trade and made him a small man whirled in the midst of something he did not understand. That was what he said in his stories and it made one of the saddest songs you'd ever heard. A song sadder than the sadness of the saddest poet. You still have a belt he made you and you hope you always will. There is fine workmanship in it. It is a simple leather belt with a brass buckle, but it has dignity in it. If a painting has a man's soul in it, so has the belt made by the cobbler who drove a sleigh up to the front and back every night. He made many things for many of the soldiers. Belts and holsters and straps of various sorts and it always gave him pleasure to see these things. Sometimes when a man was standing around, the cobbler would come to him and just run his fingers over the belt, or the cartridge box or whatever it was, then he would walk away with the satisfied dignity of a man who has done a job of work and done it well. But there was a sadness in his eyes because these unnatural circumstances, these affairs of such great international importance had robbed him of his trade.

It was the same with the organist. He was one of your great friends. A tall man with a black beard

and a straight lean face. His eyes were always
laughing, except when he heard music, then his
fingers curved and the laughter left his eyes. You
talked much about music with him. In peace time
he was a church organist in a large country town
and also gave lessons on the piano. He had been to
the conservatory and he knew Sibelius. He explained what he could of Sibelius to you one
night. You hadn't paid much attention to him before that. He was only a strange-looking soldier
who laughed at your attempts to speak Finnish and
spoke to you in English. But this particular night
you were listening to the wireless late when you
were on duty in the captain's office and nobody else
was there. The music was *Finlandia* and while you
were listening, the organist came in.

"It is the history of Finland," he told you, when
it was over. "It is all our history put to music by
the old man."

After that you listened to music together very
often. Good music from Munich and Berlin and
Stockholm, and even Moscow.

But many times when the music had finished he
would speak bitterly. One night you were listening
to the Brahms first symphony. The last movement
came, with its alpine horn winding out, solitary
and clear like cold water and then the whole joyful

triumph of the ending, and when it was over the organist stood up and threw away his cigarette.

"When there is that," he said nodding toward the radio, "why should there also be this?" and he gestured outside toward the room which was packed with wounded.

You talked with him and told him how when you first liked music you had liked Tschaikowsky and Wagner and now you didn't like them, but it was Mozart and Bach and Beethoven and Brahms and Sibelius and Cesar Franck.

"He was an organist, too," he said, smiling.

And you said that now you rather despised Tschaikowsky and Wagner for being sorry for themselves and too full of their own feelings. And he told you that those things were not important and that it was only the music which mattered and that when you boiled it down, all it amounted to was that Wagner and Tschaikowsky were not as great as the others you had mentioned, and that it was stupid for you to talk about them being sorry for themselves and that if you had not read this some place you would never have known it and would still have liked the melodies and what greatness there was in the work. And he was perfectly right. He said the most profane thing in the world to him were program notes at concerts. It was an

impertinence, he said. Music was the greatest of all
art because it was an abstract crystallization of deep
personal feeling and to say you didn't like someone's music because some obscure pedantic little
upstart said that the man had too much self-pity
was an absurdity.

But he was sad, too, because he had had to say
goodbye to this. He was sad because when there
was music there was also this other thing cutting
against it.

The end of the war came in March. You were
all sitting around the kitchen of the hospital the
night before you were waiting for the hospital
train. It was due at midnight and all the drivers
were sitting around waiting for eleven o'clock
when they'd start loading the ambulances. The big
ones. You were in charge of one of them and
O'Hara was in charge of another. Your drivers were
sitting with you in the kitchen and also many of
the stretcher-bearers. There weren't enough chairs
for everyone and so most of the stretcher-bearers
stood. It worked out that way. The drivers were all
N.C.O.'s anyway. You didn't exactly know what
you were, a cut above that, you always got a seat in
the kitchen and you only gave way to the doctors.

O'Hara was putting sugar in his tea. He put

eight lumps in. "I'm a regular Finn," he said, "see?"

"Want some bread?" You broke a big flat piece of hard bread by banging it on the table.

"Sure." He reached out for it.

One of the Lottas came and sat down. A corporal gave her his seat.

It was a blonde girl named Helme. She was a great friend of O'Hara's. He used to bring her chocolate whenever he found any. She'd been to the University of Helsinki and had helped teach O'Hara Finnish. In the beginning they'd used a phrase book and now that was one of their standing jokes.

"Hello, lemmikki," O'Hara said. Lemmikki meant darling in Finnish.

"Hello." She put some sugar in her tea.

"Would you like to go to the opera," he asked gravely, "or maybe to the ballet?" That was one of the phrases from the book.

Helme giggled.

"I would like a second-class compartment," O'Hara went on. "And I would like my baggage checked through to Helsinki."

"Have you heard the radio news?" she asked him.

He nodded.

Everybody had heard it and everybody was hold-

ing their breath over it. The news being that Finnish delegates were in Moscow and that the next
day at eleven o'clock in the morning there was to
be an armistice and that England and France were
ready to help Finland the minute the Finns asked
for help.

Everybody was excited as hell. This was it. This
was a victory. The Russians would find some way
to save face and move out, or the others would come
and finish the Russians off. Finland could hold out
another six weeks, you all thought, and that would
be enough time. None of you had been behind the
lines for weeks.

"What do you think of the news?" you asked her.

"It is glorious," she said.

The old lady who was head of the kitchen at this
hospital came over to the table.

"Hello, devil," she said to you.

"Hello, mother," you said.

The other men at the table laughed.

"I would not be your mother," she said. But she
ran her hand over your head. "That would made
me a devil, too," she said. "A she-devil."

One of the men at the table started an old joke.
"Mother is Swedish," he said to you. "That makes
you Swedish."

The old lady looked down at him. "I would

rather be a devil," she said.

"Yes," one of the others said, "mother is Swedish."

"Mother is Esthonian," another man said.

The old lady slapped him. He laughed very hard.

"This is the devil," Helme said, pointing to O'Hara.

"Oh, that one," the old lady said. "He's a troll."

"Gentlemen," O'Hara said in English. "I appeal to you . . ."

They all laughed again. Very few of them understood more than the simplest English. But they always laughed when O'Hara spoke it to them.

"Gentlemen," O'Hara said.

"Chamberlain," one of the drivers said, making out as if he was carrying an umbrella.

"Gentlemen, I give you Neville Chamberlain," O'Hara said. He was very tired and when he was that tired he always acted as if he were very pleasantly drunk. He called it his fatigue jag.

"And the days of auld lang syne," O'Hara went on. "I give you the city of New York. I give you the hotel St. Regis. Not six months ago I danced there merrily."

"Who were you with?" you asked him.

"A beautiful girl," he said. "One who loves me

truly. I was with my one great love."

"I thought I was that." Helme laughed.

"Mother is my one great love," you said. "Aren't you, lapsi?" Lapsi meant baby and this made the men laugh again. It was easy to make them laugh. And having them laugh was very pleasant.

The old lady giggled and poured some more tea.

The door opened and white frosty steam swirled in and one of the sentries came in off duty. His uniform buttons were white with frost and his face was almost purple.

"How now, good Marcellus?" O'Hara said. "How goes the watch, boy?"

The sentry tried to laugh, but his face was too stiff with cold. He took a cup of tea instead and began gulping it down, shifting from one foot to the other to warm them.

"I give you Doctor Perry," O'Hara said. "I give you the old school. I give you the Middleweller house," he went on. "Cheer now for Exeter."

"I give you Dicky Kerr," you said.

"I give you Perce Rogers," O'Hara said. "And our glorious record in hockey. Cheer for the red and grey."

"Truly, brother," you said, "this touches us all." You nodded around the table and they all laughed again.

"Friends," O'Hara said, "it's the old school spirit that counts. I trust," he added, "that all are wearing the old school tie."

"We are, brother," you said.

"Good. I will now pass among you and sell these beautiful arm bands while my colleague," he nodded toward you, "picks your pockets for a new gymnasium. Cheer now for Exeter, brothers. And may I add that the associated Harvard clubs of Pawtucket have presented this beautiful cup to be awarded to that member of the Lower Middle class who best personifies the true spirit of Exeter, and for general excellence in Latin 2. This cup is awarded this year to . . ."

"Gee, thanks," you said. "Gosh, I'm proud."

"We'd like to have you in the house," O'Hara said to the sentry who had sat down next to him. "The fellows have been talking it over and well, really I mean, we think you're ready. Of course, some of the other houses might send you bids, but, well I mean, that's up to you. Of course, if you want to hang around with a bunch of football players that's your business, but, well really I mean, we think you're all right and so just think it over, I mean. Well, you know."

The sentry pointed to O'Hara. "Huolu," he said which means crazy in Finnish.

"Gosh, Helme," O'Hara said, "I think you're a
swell girl. I was just thinking, well, what I mean is,
the spring dance is in a few weeks and it's going to
be a pretty good party, they're having Eddie Du-
chin and, well really I mean, if you could come up
to school for the dance, well gosh . . ."

The sergeant major came into the room. "All
ready," he said.

"Did the train get through?" you asked him.

"Yes."

"Thank Christ."

The train had not been able to get through for
days and the hospital was packed with wounded.
Every bit of floor space was filled.

"Ready, Errki?" you said to the driver.

He nodded and got up and began bundling himself into his clothes.

You went out in the corridor and put on your
fur coat and pulled on a pair of high felt boots and
strapped on a belt with a knife and pistol and
wrapped a scarf around your neck. You took your
cap off a peg and grabbed a flashlight and went
down to the captain's office for the papers. O'Hara
was right behind you.

After you got the papers you both went outside.

"How many have you got?" O'Hara said.

"Twenty stretcher cases. What have you got?"

"Twenty-eight sitting."

Outside the ambulances were drawn up, long and white, and men were flashing lamps, covered over with blue, at the doorways. The stretchers were being brought out to the ambulances. The air was full of frosty breath. There was the sound of men's feet crunching over the snow and the ripping sound of cold motors turning over and the vapor from the exhausts steaming. Everyone worked very quickly. It was very cold for one thing and for another you had to use too much light out there in the open.

You stood at the door to Errki's ambulance. You directed the stretcher-bearers as they slung the stretchers on the hooks inside. When they were all in, you checked over your papers. Then you gave Errki the signal to start. You stood at the side and directed him with a flashlight as he eased the big ambulance out onto the road. Then you got in next to him. After he had gone a few meters and crossed the mined bridge he turned on the headlights.

Whenever you came to crossroads or railroad tracks he slowed down and you stood out on the running-board step to see if it was all clear. You could see the other ambulances lumbering along behind you. Spaced far out.

At one crossroad you stood and listened very hard. You told Errki to turn off the lights. You could hear the planes. Very far off at first, but coming fast.

"The bastards are coming over," you told him.

The cars behind you had stopped. Their lights were off, too. You walked back to the next ambulance. O'Hara stood big and bulky and fur-coated in the road.

"We'll have to sneak in anyway," you said. "Who's in charge?"

"We are," he said. "Let's take them in one at a time. And hope these poor bastards don't freeze to death."

"O.K. Pull them in under the trees. I'll ride on the cars. You stay here."

"Right, colonel."

"Don't mention it, major."

"They're after the station," he said. "Maybe we better take turns riding them in."

"We'll talk about that later," you said.

"Trying to get the Grand Cross?" he said, but he was kidding, not angry.

"Just my numerals." You looked toward the planes. A flare dropped way off. "Get those cars the hell out of the road," you said.

He was already on his way, shouting to the drivers in Finnish, and Swedish, and swearing at them in English.

You went back to Errki. "We're going in one at a time," you told him.

He nodded and eased his clutch out. He went very slowly and you stood out on the running-board. You came around a corner and headed into the station. The planes were dropping more flares. They were heading right for the station.

The train was drawn up at the platform. It was a very long train with big red crosses painted to sides of the cars. There were many men on the platform. They were listening to the planes.

When the ambulance had pulled up, doors facing the platform, you got out.

"Where's the officer in charge?" you said.

"Here." A tall lieutenant came up to you.

You saluted, and told him who you were and what you had with you. He nodded and shouted orders. They began unloading the ambulance. Errki stood at the side and lighted a cigarette.

"Tell your driver not to smoke, please," the lieutenant said.

You went over to Errki. "He says to get rid of the cigarette."

Errki cursed and got into the ambulance. He

did not get rid of the cigarette.

They worked very quickly unloading. The lieutenant stood by giving orders. He had a beautifully disciplined crew. They worked well. The planes were very loud. Then a few kilometers away they dropped the first bomb. It made a dull deadened boomf. You did not see the flash. But you could tell it was heavy stuff they were carrying.

There were more explosions and always nearer. The ground trembled every time.

There were a lot of planes and they were flying low.

The lieutenant came up to you. "We are going to unload the train," he said. "What is the nearest hospital?"

"The Swedish Red Cross is about five kilometers."

"They have ambulances?"

"Yes, sir."

"Tell them to send them all."

"Yes, sir."

You went into the station. The first bomb dropped really close as you were going in the door. It sounded as if it had gone off in your pocket. You almost fell down.

You got the Swedes on the telephone. It took a long time for them to answer. Finally they answered. You told them what you wanted. They said they would leave immediately with six ambulances. Then you called your own hospital and told them to stand by and not send any more cars except empties. Then you went back. Just as you got outside, a bomb dropped toward the back of the train, the shock threw you down into the snow. Then they dropped five more, one after the other. The earth moved up and down under you. You could hear the metal and wood of railroad cars ripping and splintering. You got up again. The back part of the train was on fire. The train crew was working at the burning cars. There were shouts and shrieks. The flames lit everything jaggedly and threw great shadows.

The planes were circling. They were dropping everything they had. You wished you had a helmet.

You could see figures lying slantwise on the snow. The tall lieutenant was on his knees. He was hit, but he was trying to get up. Finally he did. There was blood all over his face.

You looked for Errki, but you could not see him. You could see the ambulance but Errki wasn't there.

A bomb dropped on the station behind you. There was a terrific insucking roar that pulled you backwards and you fell again, and rolled over

quickly on your face. This time you pressed right
down into the snow. Pieces of wood scattered down
around you. One piece hit you across the back.
You hardly felt it. It seemed you were down in the
snow for hours. More bombs dropped. Always the
dull boomf. They were landing mostly in the snow.
Then another one fell and made another of those
roaring exploding blast-furnace noises. There was
the sound of crashing metal. They'd hit the train
again. You laid there a few moments longer. Then
you got up. You stood there swaying for a moment.
Then suddenly you realized that the planes were
fading off. They were leaving. The ripping-cloth
sound of the motors faded away and then froze
off into the darkness.

Half the train was keeled over on its side. There
were blotches of flame all over. The station was
burning fast. The roof was caved in. The heat was
terrific.

You went toward the train. You could hardly
hear. You felt sick to your stomach. Your brain
seemed to be far off some place, but coming back
very slowly as if you were coming out of an
anesthetic.

They were all back at work now. Except the
ones lying in the snow. Four cars were almost
already burnt down to the framework. Nobody

bothered about those. They were already loading Errki's ambulance. You went up to him.

"I'll stay here," you said. "Take them to the Swedish hospital and hurry back."

Just as you finished speaking, there was the sound of a far off bomb and then another and another.

"That's the Swedish hospital," Errki said. "I'll take them to ours."

An ambulance pulled into the station yard. And then another one. O'Hara jumped out of the first one.

"You all right?" he said.

"I'm all right."

"I took them back and emptied them. They're all coming emptied."

"Swell."

For a moment you were full of admiration for O'Hara. He'd been thinking. You wondered how anybody could have thought during all that.

You both went up to the train. There were soldiers everywhere at work dragging wounded men out of the smashed cars. There were wounded all over. And fire and smashed steel and wood. There was the sound of groaning and whimpering. Many of the men working were hurt, but they kept on working. Another officer was directing the work.

"Where is the lieutenant?" you asked him.

He pointed toward one of the burning cars and shrugged.

The men brought out one of the Lottas. She was horribly smashed. They put her on a stretcher. O'Hara got two men to take her to the ambulance. There were many nurses who were hurt. There were also many in the burning cars.

Two ambulances were loaded and left. Other ambulances arrived. The work went on steadily and smoothly. Nobody spoke except to give orders. You stood with the officer in charge. They would drag somebody out of the wreck and bring the person to him. He would look them over and then tell them to take the man to the ambulances. Or else he would just shrug and they would place the person on the side of the track. Most of the time he just shrugged. Most of them were horribly smashed or burned.

You went with O'Hara toward one of the burning cars. There was a nurse lying half-in, half-out. When you got there you tried to pick her up. She was too hot. It burned your hands to touch her. Right through your gloves it burned your hands. You took hold of one of her hands finally to drag her clear. You pulled hard and fell backwards in the snow with her arm dangling in your hands.

That knocked everything out of you.

O'Hara knelt and worked his hands under her body. Then he gave a heave and lifted. When he stood up all he had in his arms was her torso and head. Her legs were under the side of the car. He let his arms drop, she landed in the soft snow with a thud. He turned and walked away. You sat there in the snow and tried to function. You tried to tell yourself that these things did not happen. Then you realized you were still holding her arm. You threw it away. It landed in the outskirts of the flames and sizzled. Then you were sick, good and hard right there in the snow. Your whole body shook in retches and you were very cold. Finally you stood up and went back to the ambulance to wait until it was loaded. O'Hara came up a little later. By the way he kept gulping for air you could tell he'd been sick, too.

Finally the ambulances were loaded and you left. There were five hundred dead. They were all lying neatly by the side of the track.

Back at the hospital it was a shambles. All the doctors were at work. The whole staff was up working. Nobody was off duty. The place was crammed with wounded. There was a steady stream of them in and out of the two surgeries. Everybody was moving.

You and O'Hara sat in the kitchen. He was very pale. You guessed you looked about the same. You were both trying to drink tea. Nobody spoke to you. They were very nice and gentle with you as if you were a harmless pair of lunatics, but nobody spoke. They moved around you. They knew something was wrong and war had taught them that when people looked like O'Hara did then you did not ask questions.

"I would like a drink," he said.

"I would, too."

"But there is no drink," he said.

"I know."

"This is a war without drink," he said.

"I know."

"Why are we here?" he said. "Is there something wrong with us? I know hundreds of people who are not here. People who are other places."

"We went to the wrong school," you said.

"Maybe that's it. Did they teach us it was our business to come to places like this?"

"I think they tried to," you said.

"Maybe we should have gone some place which would have taught us simple things. Why did we have to go to such an ideals factory?"

"It was the pictures in the chapel," you said.

"It was Daniel Webster," he said. "And the

Washington boys and the Lee boys. We should have gone to a new school like Groton and Saint Paul's. Some place without all those shining examples."

"There was too much tradition," you said.

"They sang that damn song too much. The Grapes of Wrath song."

"I know."

"Look at all the guys from our school in France. It must be the school all right. You don't catch a lot of guys from some place like Choate sticking their necks out."

"It was old Tufts," you said.

"If anything happened to us they would hang our pictures in the chapel," he said. "And talk about us just before they dismissed the seniors."

"That's it."

"And it makes us feel good to know they would," he said.

"That's it."

"There are too many ghosts hanging around Exeter. There are too many heroes hanging by their necks in the chapel."

"Maybe it was something else. Our parents maybe."

"Balls," he said. "They didn't bring us up. Exeter brought us up."

"You sound like Lew Perry."

"I just realized that he's right. They brought us up," O'Hara said. "Isn't it funny? You're a little boy and you go there and then you're not a little boy any more and they've made you into something that has nothing to do with where you were born or raised or anything. You were born in the Academy building. Huc venite and all that."

"It sounds phony."

"Then why are there so many Exeter guys in this war? Look at all of them."

"I guess you're right."

"I'll bet Boss MacKenzie would be here."

"I guess he would."

"Let's have some more tea."

"Let's."

O'Hara took a long swallow of the hot tea. "I wish I'd gone to Hun," he said.

"We're talking a lot of crap," you told him.

"Sure it is," he said. "But we believe it. And we like believing it."

"You know what that makes us?"

"I know," he said. "You don't have to tell me. Let's go and see what work there is."

"All right."

"After all," he said, "we didn't come here to sit on our cans drinking tea."

"After you, doctor."

"Thank you, colonel."

"I hate war," he said.

"I have seen war," he went on. "I know war. There will be no blackout of peace on our hemisphere. Think they'll elect me?" he said.

"You're in, brother."

"Thank you, Farley, thank you."

Then you both went on about your work which was to help undress the hundreds of wounded and have them ready for the surgery. The doctors had been on duty for fifty hours without sleep, without stopping their work except at long intervals when they would grab a cup of tea and a piece of bread and sausage.

You went down the long rows of stretchers on the floor. You carried surgical scissors and your own knife, which was razor sharp. First you had to find out where the man was wounded and work around that spot when you undressed them. Most of them were wounded in many places. One man had been brought in that morning, his leg so eaten away by machine gun fire that it looked like a piece of meat which the rats had gnawed a wedge into. The whole calf was eaten away right down to the white shining line of the bone.

In the beginning this undressing had been eas-

ier. You could cut the clothes away in any style
you wanted to because they were always thrown
away. Not now. Now every rag was saved. You
were only supposed to cut away along the seams.
Now every rag was saved. And now these men
came from the first aid posts bandaged with paper
which was very hard to wash away after the blood
and cold had crusted them to the wound.

The men's clothes were stiff with blood and
most of these men were weak. They had been
waiting so long. There were so many of them.

One man wanted water. But you could not give
him any. It was a belly wound. It was torture not
to be able to give him water. One man's testicles
were frozen hard and blue. You had seen this happen before. And you had seen the operation which
had followed. It had even made one of the doctors
sick. He was a medical man in private practice.
Everyone had been glad when the soldier had
died. It was better that way.

You worked along the lines of stretchers for
three hours or so. You were so cramped you could
hardly stand up straight. There was a pain running through your back right down to your
ankles. You could see O'Hara working on the
other side of the room. Whenever he came to an
especially bad wound you could tell by the way

his lips moved as he said to himself, "Holy Mary, mother of God . . ."

As you worked you wished you hadn't learned anything about wounds. As it was you could almost figure out their chances for getting through. A certain percentage for chest wounds, another for belly wounds, another for head wounds. The chest and the belly were the worst. Men wounded in those are practically nil. One bullet placed right in the belly perforates the whole works. Everything is coiled and compact there and one bullet put God knows how many holes in the intestines. The chest is bad too. The lungs and the heart are all a compact thing for a bullet which spreads everything as it plows through. It is amazing, though, how a man can live on with his head shattered. People's heads are made to stand great punishment. You'd seen men live after their brains had practically been spilled all over the operating table. You'd carried out waste basins filled to the brim with stuff removed from a man's head and still the man had been all right. But nevertheless you were always glad when the man had only a leg or an arm wound. Then he was all right nine times out of ten. Of course there was always shock. From cold and especially from loss of blood. As the war went on there were more and more transfusions necessary. And also more injections of salt solution. Especially on a night like that when the men had been waiting and waiting and waiting. In the back of the hospital three nurses were doing nothing but heating bottles of blood, keeping the thermometer at forty. They each had a basin with a blood bottle in it and two other basins, one of hot water and one of cold and kept pouring one and then the other into the blood bottle basin to keep the temperature steady.

There was one thing though. The infection rate was practically zero. There was no tetanus. That was mainly because so little of the soil in that part of Finland was under cultivation. There was no manure in the soil and it is this manure and other fertilizers in the soil which are the main cause of tetanus. The cold also had helped to keep the infection rate down. There was also very little gangrene. The main danger of gangrene appearing was in frozen cases and the minute a frozen part gave any indication of not thawing they amputated to stave off gangrene. The basic good health and physical fitness of the Finns was also a great thing and was nowhere more evident than in this low infection rate and low rate of shock. The diet of the Finnish soldier was very good. He got much milk and butter. They had worked over that diet at the University of Helsinki and now they were getting their dividends. If the diet of the soldiers in the French army in the last war and in this one had been proper, it is completely possible that the death rate could have been cut way down. The Finns did not work on the theory of feeding a man just to keep him going until he was hit. They worked on the theory of feeding him in such a way that he could get well after he was hit. Porridge, milk, butter, sugar, those were the main staples in Finland. Not white bread and bad meat and wine. Human life was precious in Finland. It was a thoroughly satisfactory place to be. They did not lose sight of human values even in war time. In the Finnish language, characteristically enough, the greatest word is *man*. It is a word the Finns love to use. And is used in countless combinations and greetings . . . *mies* is the word and soldier is *sota mies,* meaning war man . . . bachelor is *poika mies,* meaning boy man, which in itself is a bit of the philosophy of the Finn. The finest and heartiest peasant greeting in Finland is *terve mies,* which means hello, man.

A few hours before dawn the work slacked off. They were still going in the surgeries, but all preparatory work was done. Back in the kitchen it was crowded. Nobody wanted to go to bed, tired

as they were. They were waiting to find out about
the conference in Moscow, and waiting to see if
the news about the armistice was true. There was
an undercurrent of joy and a fierce sense of victory. A few men made jokes.

"What will we do with Russia, now we've got
it?" one man wanted to know.

There was great suspense mixed in with this
feeling of joy. The end was in sight. Nobody
doubted the outcome, but then these people never
had doubted victory.

At about five in the morning the captain called
you to his office. O'Hara was already there looking over a map. The captain looked up at you
with a sad apologetic expression. "I must send you
out again," he said. "You and O'Hara in the staff
car. The colonel is at the line and needs a car."

"Yes, sir."

"Be very careful," the captain said. "I want you
to arrive there before it is too light. I can tell you
now that an armistice is definitely decided upon
for eleven o'clock this morning."

"Jesus!" You couldn't help it.

The captain smiled. "We shall see," he said.
"Now then we will have coffee."

Coffee was brought in and the senior ranking
lieutenant came in while it was being served.

"You are ready? Good. I hope when you come back there will be peace.'"

"And victory," the captain said.

The lieutenant nodded. "Of course," he said.

"But how that is possible I do not know," the captain said.

The lieutenant did not answer. He looked at the captain and in their eyes was a sort of secret agreement.

"Anything would be a victory now," O'Hara said. "The rest of the world could think of it no other way."

"That is not important to Finland," the captain said. "What they feel in London or Paris has nothing to do with us. This is Finland and what happens is our concern, just as this war. We do not think to furnish diversions and examples for the others. We know now where we stand with them."

The lieutenant smiled. "You should understand that, O'Hara," he said. "You're Irish."

O'Hara nodded slowly. "Well," he said, "whatever happens, it isn't over."

They both nodded. "Tell me, O'Hara," the lieutenant said, "why do the Irish fight the English? They are the same people."

"They are not." O'Hara said emphatically.

"They're Anglo-Saxons, we're Celts. There's a hell
of a difference. We're older. We had a culture
while they were still painting themselves purple
with wood dye."

The captain laughed gently. "Fine," he said.
"Well, you know the route?"

"Yes, sir," O'Hara said.

"Good. You had better start warming the car."

"Yes, sir."

You both went out.

Dawn was soaking into the sky over the tops
of the trees as you passed into the advanced zone.
The soldiers in the woods were at their positions.
The men in the fox holes along the road waved
as you went by. They were smiling and shouting
things to you.

"It's like the day of the big game," O'Hara said.

"They deserve it."

"It all depends on what they're going to get."

"What do you think?"

"I don't think," he said.

"They've got to win," you said. "They've got
to have peace and win."

"You might burn a candle," O'Hara said.
"You make a great Catholic. You've got faith."

"I'm getting it."

"Me, too," he said.

"It's all these guys," you said.

"I know. It breaks your heart."

The road twisted through the woods. It was all curves. It was getting light fast.

You passed a tank at the side of the road. A soldier was leaning against the side of it smoking. It was a captured Russian tank. Now it was painted white with a blue stripe around the turret.

"That guy looks like Tim Fuller," O'Hara said. "Do you know Tim Fuller?"

"Sure."

"He's a nice guy," O'Hara said.

"They're all nice guys," you said.

"Martha's nice too," O'Hara said. "Do you know Martha?"

"Yeah. I know Martha."

"Did you ever know Eleanor Gleason?" O'Hara said.

"No."

"You ought to," O'Hara said. "She's all right."

"Well, it's too late now. Did you ever know Ann Toomey?"

"No," O'Hara said.

"She's all right, too," you said. "Did you ever . . ."

"Yeah," O'Hara said. "He's the sweetest guy I ever knew."

"He's all right when he's sober."

"Nasty jam he was in a couple of years ago," O'Hara said. "They threw him out of the Racquet Club for using his brass buttons in a pay phone."

The car was close to the line now. There was the sound of shelling. Heavy shelling.

"I think I'll write a letter to Tim Fuller," O'Hara said.

"You don't know his address."

"I'll send it to the Old Corner Book Store," O'Hara said.

"Tell them to send me Gone With The Wind," you said.

A shell landed just off the road and the snow showered up like steam.

"Maybe I won't write to Tim Fuller," O'Hara said.

"They're using up their extra stuff," you said.

"Maybe Voroshiloff's under his budget," O'Hara said.

He pulled the car in close to the trees at the edge of the road. Three shells landed in the road about a hundred meters back. You both dived into the snow. Then another shell landed a little closer. Then it was quiet.

O'Hara got up. "It was autumn," he said. "There was fighting in the hills."

Inside the tent it was very smoky. The wood in the stove was wet and the smoke made your eyes smart so that you had to keep them half shut. The shelling had started again. It was extremely heavy. Heavier than before. The shells were landing in the woods all around the tent. The tent kept shaking and there was the sound of trees breaking off and branches crashing down. It was like being in the center of a terrific storm.

"It's ten after eleven," O'Hara said. "Where's that goddamned armistice?" His voice was tight.

The tent was full of soldiers and officers. Nobody spoke much. There was an air of fearful expectancy.

There was a wireless set in the center of the tent next to the stove. It was tuned in to the government station in Helsinki. There was no firing from the Finnish side. There had been no firing since eleven o'clock. Then suddenly there was the outgoing backkicking woosh of the Finnish batteries. They had started firing again. They fired very rapidly. And then just as suddenly they stopped. And then you noticed that the nearest Russian battery had stopped, too.

"Jesus," O'Hara said. "Good gunning, boys."

"Nenonen," one of the soldiers said proudly.

Nenonen was the Finnish artillery general who was universally conceded to be the finest gunnery officer in the world. He had a system all his own and even his own officers didn't know it. But when the Finnish batteries fired, they hit what they were after.

"Bob Casey would have loved that," O'Hara said.

Other Russian batteries were still firing. You were scared. You didn't like it. You didn't like sitting there with those shells blowing hell out of the woods all around you, and you with only canvas over your head. You tried to think of other things, but every time you tried a shell came roaring over and exploded outside.

"I'm scared," you said to O'Hara.

"We're both scared," O'Hara said.

You looked at the men in the tent. They were silent and motionless. Their faces were grim, but their eyes were fierce. It was that same victorious look you'd been seeing since the night before.

"They are very ferocious now," one of the soldiers said. He spat contemptuously at the stove.

"We have not killed enough of them," another soldier said.

They were not shelling the road any more. They were concentrating on the woods.

The expressions on the faces of the officers and men in the tent changed slightly. They were colder with hate and with contempt. A lot of the joy was gone. Somewhere inside themselves they'd turned reality on again. And they looked more tired than they had a few minutes before. This particular battalion had held this position for three weeks at less than half-strength. On this particular strip of front there were thirty-five Finns all told, and they had been on duty for eighteen days, averaging perhaps three hours' sleep a day.

One of the men got up and, without a word to anyone, walked out of the tent. Shortly after he had left there came the sound of a machine-gun opening fire. The men listened. Some of them smiled. They looked toward the senior officer, a young lieutenant perhaps twenty-two or -three years old. He nodded. Several other men went out and more machine-guns opened up.

"Why not?" the officer said.

Then the radio began crackling and everyone

strained forward. In brief sentences a voice at the
Helsinki station told what peace terms were. It
was the worst possible news. The worst possible
outcome. The worst possible defeat. After a military victory in which they had forced the Russians
back everywhere except at Viborg, where in spite
of the scarehead world press, the Russians had
advanced very little since January, Finland had to
give over much, much more than the Russians had
ever asked for in the beginning.

And while everyone was still silent and sick and
cold with the unexpected shock of this, without
any pre-warning another voice came over the wireless. It was a voice everyone knew.

"Soldiers of the glorious Finnish Army." It was
Mannerheim. "I have never seen your like as war-
riors . . . from the hills of Savo to the plains of
Ostro-Bothnia. . . . I love you as if you were my
own children . . . we did not ask for war, but
once it came we acted and we acted well. Now
many thousands of the enemy stare with broken
eyes at our Finnish sky . . . the world knows that
Finland will continue to provide a bulwark for
the west against barbarism, but Finland knows she
has paid to the last penny any debt she may have
owed the west."

When he was through nobody spoke in that

tent. The somber music of *Finlandia* came over
the wireless. The officer reached out to turn the
wireless off, but one of the soldiers laid his hand
across the officer's wrist.

"Please," he said in a low voice. "Please, lutt-
nanti."

The lieutenant looked at him and then at the
others. The same thing was in all their eyes. The
same thing was in their eyes that was in Mannerheim's speech. And they listened silently to the
music of *Finlandia,* which was Finland, and they
were Finland which was *Finlandia.*

You got up and went toward the door. You kept
shaking your head and finally you had to go out.
From the pit of your stomach to the top of your
throat you were all tears and sorrow, which you
knew even then you would never lose.

The Russians had stopped firing and so had the
Finns. The Finns were out in the road. There
were about twenty of them staring over a few
meters across the line to where the road seemed
black with Russians in peaked caps. There were at
least eight hundred Russians at that one point,
staring with wonder and fear at these twenty-odd
Finns who stared back with proud hate.

You turned back toward the tent. The music

was just finishing as you entered and Tanner, the foreign minister, began to speak.

"To say you behaved as heroes," he said, "would be commonplace. You behaved as men."

The only answering sound was a harsh rasp of steel on steel. You looked up. The young lieutenant had a rifle in his hand and with deadly methodic movements he ran a ramrod through the barrel. The soldiers looked at him for a moment and then began to smile grimly.

The plane flew high over Finland toward Sweden. Far below you could see the country spread out. The forests were great green splashes glauming the white, the lakes were jagged and ice covered, the houses scattered very far apart.

"It's a good thing they passed that prohibition law," O'Hara said.

"Yeah."

"Helsinki's a nice place. Isn't it?"

"I'd like to go back there."

"We will," he said. "When our war's over."

He looked out of the window. "Christ, it's peaceful," he said. "It must have been a hell of a place to bomb."

Then the plane was out over the sea. The water

knifed between the ice in black cuts which wid-
ened as the plane flew on toward Sweden.

"The ice is breaking," O'Hara said. "The winter's over."

III

"Si quelqu'un m'a dit qu'il faut un miracle
pour sauver la France, je dirais que je crois
aux miracles parceque je crois à la France."
—PAUL REYNAUD,
after the fall of Belgium

YOU SAT WITH O'HARA IN FRONT OF THE DEUX Magots. It was Sunday and it was April and it was noontime. The newspapers at the kiosk in front of the café had big black headlines. The headlines said that the Germans had gone into Norway. All leaves in the army were cancelled. You and O'Hara were going to Brittany that night to the Polish training camp. You would join the section there to move up immediately.

"Are you sure she's gone?" O'Hara asked you.

"I'm sure she's gone," you said.

"Why?"

"I don't know," you said.

"It's rotten," he said.

"No," you said. "It's quite all right."

"Yeah," O'Hara said. "I'll bet."

"It's quite all right," you said. "Really it is."

"Where did you look?" O'Hara asked you.

"I looked everywhere," you said. That sounded silly. Or like the words to some song. . . . I looked everywhere for you, . . . 'cause I only care for you. "I mean I looked at the Petite Chaise and I called everyone up and I went by the house and then I looked in all the bars. I was very thorough," you said.

"And she's gone?"

"And she's gone."

"That's tough," O'Hara said.

"No," you said. "It's quite all right."

"Were you drunk last night?" O'Hara said.

"Yes, I was drunk. I was drunk as hell. But only after I'd looked everywhere."

"Oh," he said, "I thought maybe you'd gotten drunk first and forgotten some place."

"No," you said, "I didn't forget any place. I was at Fred Paine's and Luigi's, and all the places on the Rue St. Anne, and I was at the Colysée and the Marignan and Fouquet's and Harry's and the Ritz and the Crillon and Maxim's and Ciro's and some other places."

"You were thorough all right." O'Hara said. "Are you hung, now?"

"No, I'm all right."

"Maybe you're still tight."

"I guess I am maybe."

"You'll feel like hell tomorrow."

"Yes, I'll feel like hell tomorrow."

"Let's have another drink now," he said.

"All right."

"I was stinking last night," O'Hara said.

"Were you?"

"I feel like hell right now," he said. "Let's have champagne."

"It's an alcohol day," you said. "We can have whiskey."

"Let's have that later," he said.

"All right."

"Everybody's out of Paris," he said. "They're all at the front."

"What front?" you said.

"Well, they're all with the army."

"Oh."

"I'm sorry she's gone," O'Hara said.

"So am I," you said. "Let's forget it."

"Well," O'Hara said, "it was a good thing while it lasted."

"Sure. It was swell. Let's let it go at that."

"All right," O'Hara said. "I just wanted you

to know I knew how you felt."

"Thanks," you said. "But I'm all right. Really I am."

"I'm glad," O'Hara said. "I'm really quite glad."

"Your new uniform looks nice," you said.

"So does yours," O'Hara said. "These aspirants' stripes are really very satisfactory. I have been saluted not once but several times."

"All those Finnish insignia look very well on your uniform," you said.

"Yours, too," O'Hara said. "Especially the lion. People think we're great heroes," he said.

"I know."

"Let's have another drink," O'Hara said.

"We just had another drink."

"I mean another drink," O'Hara said.

"Oh," you said, "another drink?"

"Yes," O'Hara said.

"I see," you said. "You know, there should really be a word for another drink after you've already had another drink."

"It's a great problem," O'Hara said.

"I have thought of a solution," you said.

"I knew you would."

"If we leave here," you said, "and go to Harry's, for example, we can have a drink. It won't be an-

other drink because we've just gotten to Harry's.
It will be our first drink of the day at Harry's and
we won't have to worry about it being another
drink after another drink."

"I understand," O'Hara said. "Let us proceed,
classmate."

"Let us."

O'Hara put some money on the table. "I am
standing treat," he said.

"You mean you are flush, classmate."

"Yes," he said, "I am giving a spread in my
room tonight. Ginger beer and goodies. Everyone
is coming. Even sturdy Sam."

"Is fun-loving Tom coming?"

"Yes, classmate."

"I should be glad to come," you said.

As you walked out to the cab rank, O'Hara
said, "And while our young friends take a taxi
to Harry's bar, let us take this opportunity of
refreshing our memories as to the first forty-six
volumes in this series."

There was nobody at the bar at Harry's except
a blonde girl in a British army uniform. She sat
by herself drinking whiskey. Bob the barman saw
you when you came in.

"I thought you were dead," he said to O'Hara.

"Why, Robert. You know we wouldn't do anything like that without telling you."

"I see you've got those Polack uniforms on."

"Don't be insulting," you said.

"All the boys are with the Polacks now," Bob said. "Clark and Ottesen and you two. Do you know Vince Goodwin?"

"No," O'Hara said.

"You will," Bob said. "He's all right."

"Did you ever know Eleanor Gleason, Bob?" you asked him.

"Can't say I did."

"You ought to," you told him. "She's all right."

"Christ, you've a good memory," O'Hara said.

"Sure I have. I'll bet you never wrote Tim Fuller."

"Hullo, there," the English girl said in an American voice. "I know Tim Fuller."

"This is Joyce," Bob said. "She's a private."

"Let's fraternize," O'Hara said.

"I know you, too," the girl Joyce said. "I met you at a dance at Exeter. You had on tails and you looked scrubby."

"She knows everybody," Bob the barman said. "She even knows General Ironside."

"I really do," the girl said.

"His girl is gone," O'Hara said, pointing to you.

"Jeeze, that's too bad," Bob said. "She was a nice girl."

"She was that," O'Hara said.

"She certainly was," you said.

"Was she really?" Joyce, the private, wanted to know.

"She certainly was," you told her.

"I'm awfully sorry," Joyce, the private, said.

"It's all right," you said. "I don't mind. Really, I don't."

"Well," she said, "I just wanted you to know how I felt."

"Give me a postcard, Bob," O'Hara said. "I'm going to drop a line to Tim Fuller."

Bob gave him a postcard and set three whiskey and waters on the bar.

"Dear Tim," O'Hara said. "How are you? I am fine."

"Tell him Joyce sends her love," Joyce said.

"Joyce sends her love," O'Hara said.

"I send my love, too," Bob said.

"You don't know him," you said.

"Has he ever been in Paris?" Bob said.

"Sure he has."

"Then I know him," Bob said.

You had several more drinks.

"Where are you going now?" O'Hara asked Joyce, the private.

"I'm waiting for someone," she said.

"Ditch him," you said. "Let's go to the Meurice. You might see General Ironside there."

"I'll go," she said. "But I really know him."

"Let's go," O'Hara said. "Will you mail this for me, Bob?"

"You give me twelve francs and I will," Bob said.

"I'll mail it tomorrow," O'Hara said.

When you got to the Meurice, General Ironside was there. Joyce, the private, really knew him. She sat with him for about fifteen minutes. Then she came back.

"He said he doesn't know Tim Fuller," she said, "but to send him his love anyway. He's a terribly nice person."

"They don't come any better than Tim," O'Hara said grandly.

"I mean General Ironside," Joyce said. "I've seen plenty better than Tim."

"What are you doing in that suit?" O'Hara asked her.

"My mother is English," she said. "What are

you doing in that suit?"

"His mother was Polish," you said. "Sonia O'Sullivan."

"Let's go some place else," you said.

"We just got here," O'Hara said.

"Restless youth," Joyce, the private, said.

"Let's go some place to eat," you said.

"We can eat here," Joyce said.

"That's cowardly," you told her. "That's giving in."

"The boy is right," O'Hara said.

"I'll go any place," Joyce said. "You're nice."

"Thanks," you said.

"I don't mean you," Joyce, the private, said. "You're nice, too. But O'Hara's nice."

"Oh. I'm nice. But he's *nice*."

"That's it."

"You're in," you told O'Hara.

"I don't mind," he said. "She's nice too."

"You're nice, too," you told Joyce. "He doesn't mind."

"What's his first name?" Joyce asked.

"Sean, but you call him Johnny."

"Like Simon called Peter?"

"Let's have one for the road," O'Hara said. "And I'll tell you all about myself. Then you can do a book about us," he said to you.

"I'll do that," you said.

"Are you the one who played football?" Joyce asked O'Hara.

"That's me," he said. "Good, wasn't I?"

"I saw you play football," she said.

"I saw him, too," you said.

"Will you stop trying to horn in on the conversation," O'Hara said.

"You're a nasty insistent little man," Joyce said.

"Can't I be a friend of the family?" you wanted to know.

"Wait until we have a family," Joyce said. "Will you marry me, O'Hara?"

"Sure," he said.

"It costs ten thousand francs," she said. "Have you got ten thousand francs?"

"Sure."

"You're the first person I ever wanted to marry who did," she said. "I'm very rich."

"So am I," O'Hara said.

"So am I," you said.

"I like being rich," Joyce, the private, said. "Not that I'm a snob. I like poor people. But there's no use kidding yourself. It's very pleasant to be rich."

"I'm richer than O'Hara," you said.

"The hell you are," he said.

"What about my insurance?" you said.

"What about my grandmother?" O'Hara said.

"She's not dead yet."

"Almost," O'Hara said. "She's eighty-five."

"She's in Ireland," you told Joyce. "She's the only woman you ever heard of who came from Tipperary. I'm going to see her there. O'Hara's going to take me."

"Does he go everywhere you go?" Joyce asked O'Hara.

"He's useful," O'Hara said. "He's a fine gillie."

"Aye, that I am," you said.

"I like O'Hara," Joyce said. "I like Johnny O'Hara very much."

"I like you, too," O'Hara said. "This is a turning point."

"Isn't it so?" she said. "Let's hold hands."

"All right," O'Hara said.

"Let's go," you said. "Let's eat. The friend of the family is hungry."

"All right," O'Hara said. "Wanting to get married always works up my appetite."

"Not mine," Joyce said. "I'm not hungry."

"You don't mind?" O'Hara said. "You don't mind if I'm hungry when I fall in love?"

"Don't say things like that unless you're serious," she said.

"I'm serious," O'Hara said.

"I mean it," she said. "Please be serious, Johnny O'Hara."

"Listen," you said, "I'll be at the bar whenever you need me."

There was no one at the bar. You sat there and had a *quart champagne* and ate salted almonds.

"They're in love," you told the barman.

"Why not?" he said. "It's a nice thing."

"It's all right," you said. "But it backfires."

"I know," he said. "But most things do."

"What the hell are you? A philosopher?"

"I keep my eyes open," he said. "I see them come and I see them go. I used to see you in here with a girl all the time."

"I know," you said. "Now you see me, now you don't."

"How was Finland?" he asked.

"Cold," you said.

"It must have been."

"Sixty below," you said.

"We've had it that cold in Montana," he said.

"Pardon me," you said, "but does this Joyce girl come in here much?"

"Yes," he said, "she's a nice girl, too. She's no tramp. She used to come here with her family in peace time. She's no bum like most of them. You tell O'Hara that for me."

"He knows it," you said.

"You ambulance drivers don't know anything," the barman said.

"Are most of them bums?" you said.

"I'll say they are."

"Not the Americans."

"Especially the Americans," he said. "The good ones stay at home."

"Have a drink?"

"I'll have a sherry," he said.

"O.K. Make mine another *quart*."

A man came in and said hello to the barman and then went on into the restaurant.

"That's Vincent Sheean," the barman said. "He knows the answers."

"He likes to think so anyway," you said.

"Dorothy Thompson's here, too," the barman said.

"So am I," you said. "So what?"

"You're right," the barman said. "So what? Have one on the house."

"Sure."

Finally O'Hara and Joyce came up. You all had another drink and you left to go eat.

You ate at the Coupole. The seafood there was very good. It was the best seafood in Paris. The Coupole was full of people. Joyce knew a lot of them. Most of them were pretty terrible Mont-parnasse.

A girl came and sat with you. She was dressed very well, but she was Montparnasse, too. She had a liqueur with you and talked to Joyce about people you'd never heard of. Finally she turned to you.

"Was Finland amusing?" she asked.

"Terribly," you told her.

"Paris is not amusing any more," she said.

"You'll have to give up this sort of thing," O'Hara told Joyce.

"Have you known Joyce long?" the girl asked you.

"Years," you said, "ever since prep school."

"Has he known her long?" She pointed to O'Hara.

"Oh, frightfully long," you said. "They used to go the same place in summer."

"Where was that?"

"Oh, you wouldn't know. It's just a small place and nobody knows about it except the people who go there, but it's terribly nice. It really is."

"Do you talk like that all the time?" she said.

"Like what?" you said. "I mean, I don't know how I talk. I really don't, I mean."

"Does he always talk that way?" she asked O'Hara.

"Like what?" O'Hara said. "I mean really, how does he talk? I mean a person talks one way or another, I suppose, but really, I mean, how does he talk?"

Joyce giggled.

A man came up to the table. He was pretty god-awful, too. Studiously seedy with paint spots on his hands.

"Have you seen Tony's exhibition?" he asked Joyce. "It's simply wonderful."

"Are you an artist?" O'Hara said.

The man nodded.

"What do you paint?" O'Hara said. "I mean what kind of pictures do you paint?"

"Yes," you said. "Do you paint those terribly funny pictures with alarm clocks melting around and people without legs bustling about and, that sort of thing, you know? I mean . . . I mean, I don't know anything about art or anything, but I mean do you paint? . . ."

"You know?" O'Hara said. "Do you paint good pictures like . . . well, like people like Sargent who are civilized and, you know, well, I mean, you can tell what the picture's about? Or do you paint those fantastic things with clocks melting around and barn doors and old dead grouse and things. You know what I mean."

"How absurd," the girl said.

"Well, I was only asking," O'Hara said. "I took this course at college and we had all about art in it. You know what I mean? Slides and things about people like Leonardo da Vinci and guys like that."

"Well, Joyce," the girl said, "we really must go. Awfully nice meeting your friends. It must be wonderful to meet someone from home."

She got up from the table. The man got up, too. He kissed Joyce's hand.

"Gosh," O'Hara said, "I guess they're these bohemians or whatever you call them. Gosh," he said to the man, "do you paint naked girls and things? Nice work, huh?" He winked at the man.

The man left without answering.

"You're terrible," Joyce said.

"See? I told you he was a good gillie," O'Hara said. "Well done, my man."

"Thankee sir," you said.

"That girl was a gaudy trout," O'Hara said.

"She's very nice," Joyce said.

"I'm sure of it, Joyce," O'Hara said. "I'm sure she's frightfully nice, well, I mean, I'm sure all your friends are quite adequate."

"But that guy certainly wore fantastic clothes," you said. "And he needed a hair cut. Of course, I'm sure he was a nice guy, but well . . . You know what I mean."

"I do," O'Hara said. "I really do. He was a nice guy, but we obviously didn't have anything in common. Well, I mean. After all."

"Shut up," Joyce said. And she laughed again.

When you got outside in the street, you stood there for a moment, then O'Hara said, "Let's shoot."

"What do you think we've been doing?" you said.

"I mean let's really shoot," he said. "Let's go out to the Bois and shoot pigeons."

"O.K."

"All right," Joyce said. "Are you a good shot?"

"Terrific," he told her. "Besides nobody ever missed a pigeon in the Bois. Even he hits them." He pointed to you.

"It must be very easy," Joyce agreed.

You drove out to the Bois in a taxi and went to the pigeon-shooting place. The way they do it is they have all these tame pigeons and they let them out of cages and you shoot them for a price.

You all took shots at the pigeons for about an hour. Nobody missed. Then you got bored with it.

"Damn sporting birds, those pigeons," O'Hara said. "Very considerate. They even knew you were near-sighted."

"The coach told them," you said.

"Let's go to the races," Joyce said.

"They'll be almost over."

"No, they won't, they start late."

So you went to the races. And sat in the club-house and drank champagne. Joyce picked a horse in the race being run just after we go there.

"Are you sure of it?" O'Hara asked.

"I know the horse," she said. "We're old friends."

You looked it up on the program. She knew it all right. She owned it.

It went on all day that way. It was really fun. She was a swell girl all right and she liked O'Hara and he liked her and you liked them both even if the fact that your girl was gone made you feel a little like the emasculated man in The Sun Also Rises which O'Hara always said should have been called Our Neutral Friend.

You had cocktails at the Ritz and dinner at the Relais Plaza and finally you were at the Gare Montparnasse and everything was a shambles of men in uniforms carrying kit bags and helmets and gas masks and there were the gendarmes looking at your papers and a tangle of Polish being

spoken that sounded like the Chicago stockyards.
Some transportation officer came up to you and
clicked his heels and told you his name which had
a "sky" at the end and then about four more officers came up and you and O'Hara and Joyce
were the center of a bunch of Pole officers all
clicking their heels and doing that two fingered
salute and saying their names. It kept going on
"thisky" "thatsky" "whichsky" "whatsky" until
O'Hara bowed gravely and said, "O'Harsky." And
everybody was happy.

There were people saying goodbye to each other
all over the place and it was different than it had
been so far during the war because now the French
knew that the war had begun in earnest. And
goodbye this time probably meant goodbye.

Joyce came out on the platform with you and
she and O'Hara stood there looking grave and
very sad and you were suddenly glad your girl
had gone away.

"Look," you said, "I'll dive in and get us a seat.
So long, Joyce."

"So long," she said. "I think you're nice, too."

"Be a good girl," you told her.

"Be a good boy. I'll send you some chocolates."

"O.K. So long."

You climbed on the train and found a seat in

a compartment and put your stuff all over it.
The aisles were full of men walking back and
forth and shouting. They were mostly Polish. The
train was packed because all leaves had been cancelled and everybody was pretty excited. Every
guy on that train thought he was on his way to
Norway.

You looked out of the window and you saw
O'Hara suddenly grab at Joyce and kiss her long
and hard and they clung to each other and then
she pushed him away and walked off.

O'Hara came into the compartment and sat
down.

"That's a nice girl," you said.

"She is."

"You've got a good thing there."

"I know it."

"It's probably the kind of thing that'll stick."

"I know it."

"Well, you're lucky."

"Am I not?"

"Aren't you glad?"

"Sure I'm glad." Then he lit a cigarette.
"Godammit," he said. "Why does everything happen to me?"

Then the train began to pull out and everybody stood at the windows and shouted to people on the platform.

"Goddammit," O'Hara said again.

"Forget it," you told him.

"Yeah," he said. "That would be very nice."

Then the next day you were in your ambulances and your ambulances were on flat cars and there were many freight cars full of soldiers and the whole division was moving up to the north of France. And after that you were in many villages and the country was beautiful with the spring and there was Nancy and Vezelize and Luneville and Domremy and Deuze and Kappelkinger and Albestroff and Ventzviller and roads winding up the Vosges on spring mornings and there were many binges and many fights and the war went on and got worse and worse, it went from one defeat to another and then came Dunquerque and the French were left alone to face the steamroller and on it came and you were pulled out of the division and attached to the Matchek Brigade and sent to the battle of the Somme to stop the German advance and it was almost the battle of the Marne before you got there.

There was walking along the main street in

Favières on spring evenings after dinner with the
dusk falling dimly and the Polish soldiers lined
up to say their prayers in front of the church and
there were those clean wet spring mornings driving out toward Colombier and Nancy and Neufchateau when you met company after company of
Polish infantry marching along, singing as they
went, and inside you something would lift high
and you were full of faith and all your doubts
faded.

The Poles sang a lot. One night you had the
cars drawn up on a street in a town near Vezelize
and the Poles in that sector were moving up. It
was very dark and the street was crowded with
men in full pack and they were singing the age
old songs of Poland, songs full of bravery and
simple faith and love for their country. They sang
beautifully and later they fought as well as anyone
had fought before and most of them gave their
lives affirming what they had sung. Except for the
Finns you had never in your life seen anyone who
loved their country as much as the Polish soldiers.
In the beginning that night it had seemed all un-
real. Too much like the movies, these dark shadowy
groups of helmeted soldiers and the sudden gusts
of light fanning from opened bistro doors and slow
mounting songs and the dispatch riders and the

dull gleaming of metal on guns and on intrenching tools; but then it had gotten to you and it all became one of those few moments when it was absolutely clear to you why you were where you were and why of all the places you had ever been it was the best.

And there was the day when the first Polish division formally became a part of the fourth French Army. It was a rainy grey day and there was a review of the whole division just outside of Neufchateau and it took hours until finally your cars rolled past the reviewing stand and you had a sudden burst of the *Polonaise* in your ears and a sudden swift glimpse of General Sikorski in his short polo coat.

There were many air raids. The first one was rather funny because when it began and everybody put on helmets and came out into the street and stood in the shelter of walls to watch, one of your people came dashing out and stood in the center of the street without a helmet on his head. But instead he had placed a small American flag there.

There was the morning the division arrived at Vezelize to go from there to the various surrounding towns where it would be billeted and the German planes came over and put dashes of white smoke on the sky over each of these towns just to show they knew where the towns were. And after that every time the division moved the German radio would announce it and tell you where you were going.

And there was that night in the mess just before you were sent off to join the Matchek Brigade when you had some Polish officers in after dinner and they brought soldiers with musical instruments along with them as their share of the party. The Polish officers were very poor after the invasion of Poland and had no money even for drinks and even had to rely on the generosity of the American ambassador's wife for enough cigarettes. But that night they furnished the music and you all sang and they sang Russian and Polish folk songs and it was like something out of Tolstoi. Those officers were among the people trapped at the Maginot Line when the Polish first division had to fight its way out through the German lines in groups of four or five and it was also from this division that the thousand Poles came who sacrificed themselves to cover the retreat from the Line and went down fighting, every last one of them. In spite of treachery, the majority of the Poles were fine. The French gave them the worst of the rations, the worst of the equipment, the

worst of the billets, and in the end gave eighty-five
per cent of them the privilege of dying in the
worst of the fighting. A few of the French generals
were for them. De Gaulle was and now they're
with De Gaulle, what's left of them, fighting on in
England while the French generals who spoke of
them with contempt and treated them with worse
and wouldn't heed Matchek's advice which was
the same as De Gaulle's, those French generals
are still as far from the fighting as they ever were.
They let the Poles be sacrificed and they let their
own men be sacrificed. They knew the soldiers
would be brave and they were. And now the generals are playing at being generals and holding
trials in France. The traitors are trying each other,
and using the whole Guarde Mobile to keep them
a safe distance from the soldiers they betrayed.
There is a great lesson in military affairs to be
learned from this, the difference between generals.
You pays your taxes and you takes your choice.

There was that night at Orsay on your way
to the front when you had the cars parked deep
in the woods among the armored cars, radio trucks
and motorcycles and you slept in your sleeping
bag out under the trees and woke up suddenly
hearing the drone of planes and the throaty crack
of your D.C.A. It was a clear night sanded with

stars and there were the long beams of the search-
lights fingering the sky and then you heard the
soft whistling swishswish of the broken anti-aircraft
fragments falling down all around you and the
earthy boomf of the bombs and there you were
lying on your back in the woods only half awake
and plenty scared and then you put your helmet on
and went back to sleep. The next night they came
over again and blew up the place a half hour after
you had left.

And there was that night only a few days before the very end when you drove to Thouars to
pick up the Polish wounded who had been left
behind there. The Germans were on both sides of
you that night and there was only a small opening
behind you to get through and Thouars ahead of
you and the question was would they take Thouars
before you got there and cut off your retreat before you could get back?

You drove into Thouars in the early morning
and up to the hospital. There were only nuns left
with the wounded and the Germans were coming
in the front end of the town and the courtyard of
the hospital was stacked with the dead like cord
wood and the corridors were full of bloody cloth-
ing from the dead and you loaded up the ones who
might still live and the nuns stayed behind to give

absolution to the dying and they gave you coffee and bread and kept murmuring "Pauvres messieurs."

And there was the beginning of all the American ambulance units in Paris in the fall when the wrong men had gotten hold of the thing and it was riddled with rotten Ritz Hotel corridor intrigue and loud boastings by fat-bellied old men and when they finally sent a section to the front they didn't even bother to forward their mail to them and were all running around Paris in fancy uniforms calling each colonel and major and captain and when you got back from Finland they bawled you out for not having gotten enough publicity. They were angry because you'd stayed at the front working with the Finns. That day you'd thought O'Hara would kill the man who was head of the service. But instead you both quit and joined a section that meant something, that wasn't out for publicity, that carried out in its whole organization the sincerity which every ambulance driver felt in his heart. That was because it was Ted's section and that was the way Ted felt. Of course Ted was just a kid and he wasn't trying to get the Legion of Honor. He was just a kid, you understand, and didn't know about all these fancy deals you could pull off in the name of humanity.

He didn't realize that you could use the death
struggle of places like Finland and Poland and
France to get publicity for yourself. He thought
he was a soldier. And he was. And he was a
damned good one. But these others were just
like the treacherous officers and fifth-column mem-
bers of governments and had a swell time in
swell uniforms and gave out interviews and some
of them even commuted back and forth between
Paris and the Waldorf Astoria and told fat rich
old women all about the horrors of war and everything they said and did and were wasn't as valid
or as worthwhile as one tiny louse from the seam
of one of their drivers' pants. Nobody was spared
from the rottenness that was all over France. There
wasn't anyone who wasn't betrayed one way or another. There were few organizations of any sort,
neutral or belligerent, which didn't have traitors
and opportunists in very high places. When it
spreads it spreads fast and nothing is spared from
contagion. But the drivers like the soldiers went on
in spite of it and fought for what they believed
in and that's what can't be beaten. Not by anyone.
And there are still enough untenanted graves left
for anyone who wants to try. And it will always be
that way. And if at the end of time there is one
traitor left, then you can be sure there will also be

one man left to finish him off. The last man left
on earth won't be a traitor and maybe that's why
you go on fighting and dying.

And there was Nancy with its old grey stone
buildings and gates and the gilt tipped black iron
railings and the gold clock of the Place Stanislaus.
And the Palais de Bierre and the Brasserie Uni-
verselle and the childish pleasure you got from having ice in your Pernod there and the let-out-of-
school feeling of being able to spend a couple of
hours in Nancy once drinking Pernod and watching the pretty girls. Nancy was filled with them,
girls from all over France who had been evacuated
there. The red light district in Nancy huddled up
against the walls of the cathedral and the houses
had numbers painted to them and the numbers
signified the difference in the quality of the mer-
chandise.

And there was the little Polish cavalry sergeant
in Croixmare who wanted to know, "How are the
Philadelphia Athletics making out?" He'd come to
France in '17 with the American Army and after
the war he'd gone to Poland and fought with Pil-
sudski and stayed in the Polish army afterwards and
been there fighting the Germans and had gotten out
through Roumania. His parents were Polish and
his father worked in the Chicago stockyards. You

and he felt very pleased about both being from
Chicago. And there was the bistro in Colombier
owned by the American who'd stayed in France
after the last war. He was from New Orleans and
once he'd taken his wife to America on a visit and
she never tired of telling about Washington and
Memphis and New Orleans. And there was the
Polish camion driver who was born in Detroit. He
knew no English and could only point to himself
and grin and say, "Detroit of Michigan."

And there was Artur Rodzinski's nephew who
was a fine mechanic. He was in your division. He
spoke very good English and was pleased when
you told him what a fine conductor you thought
his uncle was. He'd been at the London School of
Mines when the war broke out.

And there were the daily arguments at the mess.
Some of the section was anti-British and the arguments were fierce, especially after Dunquerque
Everyone liked the R.A.F. even then, but there
was the feeling of having been let down by the
British army. And one night there was a regular
pitched battle after dinner over the singing of *God
Save The King*. The navy was all right, too. Everyone conceded that. But all winter or fall everyone had come into contact with the British army
officers in Paris and these officers were very super-

cilious and very condescending about the French
and, worse than that, about the Poles, and after
Dunquerque the resentment boiled over. No matter what Dunquerque had seemed to statesmen and
civilians, it could only seem one thing to the men
left behind to face the Germans. The thing no one
could forgive them was that they'd left all their
material behind and had not destroyed it. That
made anything Churchill said about a great retreat very hollow, especially when you knew that
all those trucks and tanks were going to be used
against you. Maybe it's a good thing all those
British soldiers were evacuated before the final
smash, but on the other hand there is always the
possibility that if England had sent the number
of divisions she'd promised the smash would never
have occurred. Now all one can do is hope that
when the British army goes into action again,
which it will have to do before England can win
any offensive action (and it's offensive actions not
great defensive struggles which win wars) its leader-
ship will be better than it was and one can only
hope that England too has learned the uselessness
of amateur officers. The R.A.F., remember, was
in the beginning officered and manned by professional soldiers and many of these twenty-two and
-three and -four year old boys had already had five

and six years of service. Many of the observers and
gunners and ground men had been in the R.A.F.
since they were fifteen years old. So that when war
came, they were veterans, even though they were
only twenty-two or so. The R.A.F. was not caught
unready so far as its personnel went. They went
about their job coolly and professionally. And they
were in France before war was declared and long
before that knew where their bases and fields and
sectors would be. The army, on the other hand,
had as the majority of its officers territorials, officers with a few months' summer training, and no
matter what they felt in their hearts, which no one
doubts, it was not good enough. You had to know
your job. And, it is not unreasonable to say, England should have known this. Everyone should
have known it. Ignorance is no excuse and the
only facts which remain when everything is finished
are victory or defeat and it is childish to debate
the moral issues involved in gaining victory. Victory, no matter how it is gained, is better than defeat. This may not apply to football games, but
war is not a game. If you believe that what you are
fighting for is right, then any means you use to
gain victory are excusable.

Therefore, in spite of the record of the R.A.F.
and the number of planes going to England, one

wonders what about tanks and guns and armored cars and motorcycles. What about the infantry? Or is the expeditionary force which will carry the war into Germany going to be an American one?

These were the things you argued in the mess back in April and May of 1940. Every day you argued these things. What is a nation as sentimental as England, a nation who nurses the Chamberlains kindly long after the horrible results of their blunders are apparent, going to do when she has to attack?

And you used to argue about generals and you used to hope that this war would produce some great generals on your side so that it wouldn't reduce itself into another war of attrition which, as the French officers told you, was the result only of incompetence and blundering. Verdun was a blunder and it was only the determination and heroism of the soldiers which made it into anything else. The last great generals in the world were Americans like Grant and Lee and Forrest who, "got there fustest with the mostest men." And the German tactics in this war much more resemble the War Between the States than they resemble 1914–18. And Mannerheim was a great general, but he, too, was an attacker, a guerilla fighter like George Rogers Clark or Marion. Mannerheim was no Foch, no Pétain. One reason the little countries like Finland and Greece are able to put up such a heroic show is that these little countries attack, attack, and attack again. The big countries, except for Germany, have not yet tried this. An air-raid shelter can be built overnight. A tank cannot. These are lessons which should have been learned.

As early as April, when the results of Norway had begun to be learned, the hope for victory began to leave the army and a ready-to-die fatalism set in and, as it did, the more and more open became the traitors, and finally the whole thing blew up and fell apart into rotten crumbling bits.

And it all wound up with you sitting on that dark road watching the French retreat go by and waiting for orders to move up to Epernay which was on fire.

Finally the column began moving again up toward the artillery fire. You came into a town with flares dropping all around and stopped the car. A French lieutenant came out and wanted to know where the hell you thought you were going. And you wanted to know where the hell the rest of the Brigade was and you said you were going on up until you found them and he said you were not because the Germans were five hun-

dred meters away and where was headquarters and
that this town you were in was technically speaking no-man's-land. In other words you were smack
in the center of a battlefield and you could not
find your own army. Somebody had really bitched
things up for fair.

The lieutenant started off to find headquarters
in the town and you were sent with him. The place
was empty and silent and dark except for the
flares and gun flashes beyond the town and in the
hills around it. The French lieutenant had some
trucks and very few men and that's all there was
in the bloody place. It was a hell of a thing to
stop to think about. Every time you came to a
street corner you expected to see German motorcycles come tearing around it or tanks or armored
cars. It was not fun.

It was a long walk to the headquarters. A long
walk down dark streets lit white and clear every
once in a while by the drifting down of parachute
flares. The French lieutenant walked ahead. He
had his pistol drawn. There was shelling and
bombing. They were shelling with seventy-fives.
The bombs were small ones.

You passed a church. The steps were high and
broad and curved out at the bottom where they
met the street. The church was big and grey and

gaunt, then a flare dropped and flattened out against the wall on the opposite side of the street. You could see the church immense against the sky.

It was absolutely silent in the town itself. It was frightening walking through this deserted town. The lieutenant walked very carefully. He kept looking up and down the side streets.

Finally you came to a house with chinks of light showing through the shutters. You could hear loud talking inside. The lieutenant stopped and knocked at the door. No one answered. He knocked again. Still no one answered. So he kicked and the door flew open. He went in and you followed him.

There were six or seven officers inside. Some were French and some were Polish. They were all very drunk. There was a case of champagne in the center of the floor and many empty bottles. There were maps scattered over a table. There was a field telephone.

A drunken Polish colonel with a sweaty shaved head staggered up to the lieutenant and asked him who he was. He kept poking his finger at the lieutenant's tunic bottons. The lieutenant pushed him away and he fell backwards over the champagne case. He sat down among the empty bottles.

The other officers laughed. The Polish colonel shouted that he would have the lieutenant court-martialed. The lieutenant told him to shut his mouth. The other officers laughed again and offered the lieutenant champagne.

"Who is in command?" the lieutenant asked. He spoke very disdainfully. He was overstrung and half crazy with fatigue and hunger and the bombing and the shelling, but he was a St. Cyr officer and he could not keep the disdain out of his voice when he talked to these others, who were reservists. One of them was a member of the Chamber of Deputies. The lieutenant told you that.

"Who is in command?" he asked.

They all tried to talk at once. Finally the Chamber of Deputies man who was a major said that he was second in command to the Polish colonel.

"You will evacuate at once," the lieutenant said.

"That is absurd," the major said. "Why?"

The lieutenant told him that the Germans had broken through and were just outside the town.

Somebody in the room laughed. It was a triumphant laugh. The lieutenant's face tightened.

"Who laughed?" he asked.

Then the laughter came again. It was the Polish colonel with the shaved head. The lieutenant walked over, his pistol held stiff out before him.

"Was it you, monsieur?" he asked with deadly politeness.

The Pole shrugged insolently.

The lieutenant looked at him for a minute. Then he shot the Pole in the stomach from four yards away. The noise was very loud. The Pole crumpled over the champagne bottles and blood soaked over the floor under him.

"You will evacuate immediately," the lieutenant told the others. Then while they still stared stupidly at the dead Pole he took the maps from the table, saluted, and quickly left the room.

Now it was easy to understand the delay and the bitched up orders.

The shelling was closer and the flares were landing with less of an interval. They were like clear white stars floating down burning brighter and brighter as they came. Where they landed they lit everything up like a movie set.

When the lieutenant got back to the cars he sent a detail to arrest the headquarters officers and gave orders for them to shoot anyone who made trouble. Then he told the section to go to Sezanne and look for a dressing station there and wait there for orders from the brigade.

O'Hara came up. He carried his overcoat slung

over his shoulder like a sack. It was full of champagne bottles. He passed them out to the section. Everyone got three or four bottles. Everyone needed it.

Shells were landing at the edge of town and in the town itself. The detail arrived with the arrested officers. They were all there except the Polish colonel.

The lieutenant set up his four machine-guns facing the four streets which converged on the square in the direction from which the Germans were coming. He had his trucks parked in a line across the square with the machine-guns in between them. The rest of the men scattered and lay on their bellies across the cobbles in position to fire under the trucks. Then the lieutenant lined up the officers he had arrested. He lined them up in front of the machine-guns, facing the Germans.

You began backing the ambulances around and started back the way you'd come and that was the last you saw of the lieutenant. The fifth-column officers stood in a line in front of the machine-guns. They were still pretty drunk and they looked pretty foolish. But the dead colonel had done some job. He had broken the brigade in half, cut off its supplies and communications, evacuated its first aid post hours before the attack began, and then sent thirty-eight hundred men in to fight tanks with rifles and bayonets.

O'Hara climbed in next to you. You were in the last car.

"Want me to drive?" he asked.

"Not yet. But open some of that champagne."

The shelling became louder and louder as you rattled through the dark town after the car ahead of you. You could see the shell bursts in your rear view mirror.

O'Hara passed you a champagne bottle. You took a long swallow. It felt good. You put the bottle on the floor next to you.

The road was empty except for your cars. The retreat had passed out of the way and the Germans had nothing between them and Sezanne except the French lieutenant with his four machine-guns and your ambulances. There were still French troops somewhere, but you guessed there weren't many. If the Poles were there they would fight, they were good soldiers. But everything looked pretty bad.

"Want me to drive now?" O'Hara said.

"Yeah."

You stopped and O'Hara changed places with you. Then he raced ahead in the darkness to catch up with the others.

"Well, they crossed the Marne," O'Hara said.

"Yeah."

"Jesus," he said.

"Yeah."

"Some shambles," O'Hara said.

You didn't talk much after that. You were filled with a feeling of cold desperation. It seemed as if it was a showdown for everything in the world that was any good. Your head ached and you were tired and your stomach was empty and you didn't care any more about anything except wanting somebody somehow to stop the Germans. And you wanted to sleep. Very much you wanted to sleep. And you wanted to live. Very much you wanted to live.

The medical headquarters at Sezanne was abandoned. It was an old chateau deep into the woods. It had been abandoned for hours. There was the remains of a meal on a table and there were many smashed boxes of medical supplies and a heap of red cross brassards. It was another silent deserted place. You all stood there and wondered what to do. Finally you went back to the main road and parked the cars outside of town facing away from Sezanne.

There was a tremendous stream of retreating French soldiers pouring through. It was like watching one of those twelve-hour parades. Hundreds of pieces of horse-drawn artillery and wagons and foot soldiers. At first it was just a sullen line of men falling back. They didn't say much. They looked very tired. Then a change came slowly over and the men were more excited. They were scared. They kept shouting to you to fall back. The Germans were right behind them, they said. The Germans were shooting everyone they caught. They were taking no prisoners. Fall back, they kept telling you.

But so far you'd seen no Polish soldiers and so there was no falling back. When the Poles retreated, you'd retreat. Not until then.

There were many Belgian soldiers in this mob of retreating men. Some of them had walked all the way from Brussels. Two British soldiers came by. You yelled to them and they came over. They were completely done in and you gave them drinks, all you had left to drink. One of them was just out of the hospital. You put him in the back of one of the cars and told him to take a rest. The other British soldier talked to you out in the road. He was from one of those "line old regiments." They'd shot seven out of ten of their own officers at Amiens. They had arrived at Amiens and when the news came that the Germans were fifteen miles away, the colonel had gone back to Dunquerque

and left his men behind. Then he'd come back
again and told them they were to surrender and
they shot him and six other officers. This regiment had then fought its way from Amiens to
Dunquerque and helped cover the British retreat.
When they arrived at Dunquerque they had been
told they could not be evacuated with the rest of
the British because technically they were not part
of the B.E.F., but had been gazetted to the fourth
French Army and so, after watching the rest of the
British being taken home to England, they had
had to fight their way back to Amiens. And this
soldier was the last man left so far as he knew. He
had been traveling over the back roads at night
right through the German lines time and time
again. He was only doing what ninety per cent
of the whole army was doing, looking for headquarters.

"The British Army is all right," this soldier said,
"but there are too bloody many colonels."

You talked to Belgian soldiers and they said the
same thing about their army. It was the same thing
the whole way up and down the allied armies. The
artillery pouring through Sezanne had not been
able to fire a shot because they had been sent shells
for 155's and their batteries were 75's.

The Black Watch at Amiens had gone in against

the tanks with bayonets and an unarmed piper walking fifty yards ahead playing Loch Lomond and they came back with the same piper playing Roamin' in the Gloamin'. The Scots had been magnificent. They hung in the tops of trees and dropped on the tanks with lighted petrol. The French had fired their 75's point blank until the barrels were red hot. The Poles had faced tanks with rifles. But everybody had been betrayed. And everybody felt it and there was nothing to do. Every time you took up a position, whether it was for a hospital or a heavy battery, you were bombed right out of it. There were no allied flyers in the air. They were in trucks on the roads, squadron after squadron of them falling back.

The cars were parked about one hundred yards from a petrol dump and right in front of the petrol dump was a French anti-aircraft battery.

While you were talking to the British soldier, German planes came over. You all dived into a field of four-foot-high wheat. The planes circled over and bombed the road and machine-gunned the town. There were one hundred and fifty planes in that flight. There was no firing from the anti-aircraft battery. It had been abandoned the night before and the guns left behind. They had also

left hundreds of liters of petrol behind. in that
dump with only one old decrepit reservist to
guard it. He had an 1880 rifle. It was heartbreak-
ing.

You were down on your side in the wheat. It
felt very sheltered and safe there. Except when the
ground quivered under you. The machine-gun
fire was hitting pretty far away from you. A hand
came around through the wheat. The hand held
a package of biscuits.

"Here," O'Hara said, "have some."

"Thanks."

"Some stuff."

"Yeah."

You could hear your people talking all around
you there in that wheat field. Talking in low
voices. Trying to keep their voices steady. You
were all beginning to feel punch-drunk.

Then the planes were gone and you stood up.
The road was not pretty. There were a lot of dead
horses and smashed caissons. Some of your people
were helping a man who was shot in the stomach.
He died while they were trying to get him into
an ambulance.

The section leader came over to everyone with
a bottle of champagne. He smiled foolishly. "I just

remembered," he said. "It's my birthday. I'm twenty-one." He laughed. "Today I am a man," he said.

You all drank champagne and wished him happy birthday and then more planes came and you went back into the wheat. One of the section stood out in the road taking pictures.

"What's wrong with you guys?" he yelled. "You'd pay a buck and a half for this at Roxy's."

There were thirty-five planes this time. They looked very snotty flying up there. Lying on the ground you felt like the lowest thing that moved. Like a worm or a ready-to-be squashed bug. And that's just what you were.

Then one French plane came out of the clouds after them. It was a Curtiss P 40. The Curtiss sailed right into the clouds after the thirty-five Germans.

"He must have been a pretty nice guy," O'Hara said.

You lay there while they flew over. There was the sound of distant bombing.

"Civilization," O'Hara said, "it's wonderful."

"Yeah. Yeah. Yeah." You were all shaken up inside. You were trying to get hold of yourself. Trying to keep from cracking up. Trying not to be scared. At least trying not to show it. You wished

O'Hara would shut up.

"Don't mind my talking," O'Hara said. "I just can't help it."

Then the planes were gone again. The section leader told you and O'Hara to go into town and buy some food if you could. You went. You were glad to have something to do besides watching the retreat pour through, shouting to you to run away.

You walked into the town past the retreat. The French kept shouting to you to go the other way. O'Hara cursed and shouted back at them.

"You yellow bastards," he said to them. "You goddamned dirty yellow sons of bitches." He was almost crying. "I wish we could start running away," he said. Then he began yelling at the French again. "You lousy bastards," he yelled.

The town was packed with men. They wandered around aimlessly or stood on street corners arguing. Many of them were talking revolution. Many officers were with them. They were shouting things like Down With Daladier, and Down With Blum, and Down With Capitalism. They were most of them drunk. There were many drunken Algerians and Senegalese. They were beginning to turn ugly. It was no place to be.

You stopped at one store. It was filled with soldiers, mostly black. They were looting the place.

When you started in, one of them pointed a rifle at you and told you to beat it. You beat it.

Finally you found a store where nobody stopped you from going in.

"Here we go," O'Hara said.

You pushed your way into the store and began to take things off of the shelves. That's what everyone else was doing. They were stuffing their musette bags with everything they could lay their hands on. You and O'Hara went right to work. You filled your pockets with tinned things. Lobster and shrimps and salmon and beef. You took several bottles of Kirsch and a couple of bottles of Marc. It was the only liquor left. O'Hara took lots of boxes of biscuits and some oranges and some cheap pink and white candy.

Suddenly somebody nudged you. It was a Senegalese infantryman.

"Yes?" you said.

He pointed to a high shelf where there was a can of beans.

"You get it, mon lieutenant," he said in a nasty voice and pointed to a ladder going up the shelves.

"You better do it," O'Hara said.

"I guess so."

You started up the shelf and finally got the can. Then you started down. Then you began to get mad. All the bombing and double-crossing and you running around sticking your neck out for somebody else's country and the somebody else was running away and now this black son of a bitching nigger wanted to be tough. O.K. You'd be tough too. It all went through your mind in a minute, hell, you were tough. You'd been to Finland hadn't you? Where the hell had this black bastard been? He was running away. You came down the ladder slowly. Then you turned near the bottom.

He was standing there. His eyes were bloodshot.

"O.K., you black son of a bitch," you said.

"Watch it," O'Hara said suddenly.

"Shut up," you said. "No nigger's going to give me orders. No fat black monkey's going to tell me what to do."

All this time the Senegalese was watching. He held his hand out.

"Here it is you son of a bitch," you yelled and you let fly with the can and it hit him smack in the nose and knocked him down.

Nobody else did anything. For once nobody ganged anybody else. They were all too busy.

The Senegalese was still down. And you were bloody tearing mad. You pulled your pistol out.

"I'm going to kill me a nigger," you said. Then

you began to kick the Senegalese before he got up. His nose was smashed in where the can hit him and blood was on his face and this time he was scared. You kicked him hard in the chest.

"There are still officers in this army," you yelled. "This isn't any revolution yet." And you kicked him again.

"Let him go," O'Hara said.

"I'm going to kill the bastard," you yelled.

"O.K.," O'Hara said. "Kill him. But do it and let's get going."

"O.K." You clicked off the safety of the pistol. It was a mauser you'd brought back from Finland and it was big and murderous looking.

The Senegalese was up now and he started running for the door.

You started shooting. "You black son of a bitch," you kept screaming, and fired all eight bullets in the clip and missed him.

"Hi yo, Silver," O'Hara said. "Let's go."

The other soldiers were standing around looking at you. They weren't angry and they weren't friendly. That retreat was really one of those times when it was every man for himself.

"You still felt tough. "— yourselves and your whole families," you said.

"Cafard," O'Hara said pointing to you. They

all nodded and he pushed you out of the store.

You walked down the street together. You were still mad, but you were also tired.

"I'm sorry, Johnny," you said. "I just got fed up."

"When you blow your top, you really blow," he said.

"Boy, I really wanted to kill that nigger."

"I know," he said.

"I'm a lousy shot," you said.

"You were shooting high. That gun kicks the barrel up. You knew that."

"I'd have hit him with a parabellum."

"Sure you would have," O'Hara said. "I know that."

"He's a lucky nigger," you said.

"Sure he is."

You walked along for a while. The streets were still full. They were still talking about revolution and what had happened to the armament tax money and the work done under the decree laws and they were still shouting about Daladier. The retreat was still choking through and horses were kicking hell out of windows and staggering and slipping on pavements and wagons were turning over.

Out on the main road it was still a shambles.

There was a lot of wreckage on the road and some corpses.

"Well," you said, "here goes democracy."

"You're some democrat," O'Hara said.

"O.K.," you said. "Forget it."

"Well," O'Hara said, "you can put your gun away now. You're not back in Chicago."

When you got back to the cars everybody came around to get the liquor. Nobody gave a damn about the food.

"Meet Two Gun Butch," O'Hara said.

The retreat was thinning out. It was thinning out to a trickle of stragglers. Then somebody shouted and pointed and you saw three soldiers in dark brown berets. They were Poles. Somebody grabbed them. The liaison officers and one of your people had gone off looking for headquarters. You never saw either of them again. But luckily the Poles spoke French. Where was the Brigade? They shrugged blearily. They were the Brigade. You were the Brigade. Out of thirty-eight hundred men all that was left was four privates and eight American ambulance drivers. They'd taken their position in the dark and there had been a lot of artillery and the next thing they knew they were between two tanks and all their ammunition was gone and a French officer had yelled to them to run. "Sauve qui peut," he yelled.

You rushed the cars over to the gasoline dump and began loading big fifty-liter drums into the cars. Everybody got about two hundred liters. It was obvious now that unless a position was taken up at the Seine this shambles might end in Bordeaux. Actually it ended at Hendaye a lot further on.

Then you began to load soldiers into the cars. You packed the cars with French soldiers. Chasseurs Alpins mostly and mostly from the same regiments. They were all right, those Chasseurs. They'd stuck together. They said that headquarters of the 4th division was in Nogent. You decided to report there with your Poles. You were the Brigade. The cars were packed and there were men standing on the running-boards and sitting on the fenders. They weren't wounded men and they all had rifles. You had a big Chasseur sergeant sitting next to you. He had a loaded light machine-gun across his knees. None of you stopped to think what would happen to you if you were caught carrying armed soldiers.

The Germans were coming in the far end of Sezanne when you started off down the road. You drove like hell for about half an hour. You headed toward Nogent. As far as any one of you could tell

there would probably be hell's own battle at Nogent that night or the next morning. Also so far
as you could tell you were the rear guard of the
Polish army and that probably went for the French
army too. Seven ambulances, four Polish privates,
about ninety or a hundred Chasseurs Alpins, and
yourselves. And you were the only officers. That
was certainly a rear guard unique in military history. It was a nice finish to the third battle of
the Marne.

You didn't hear the planes when they came. You
saw the cars ahead stop short and you stopped and
then you heard them. You opened the rear door
of your ambulance and told the soldiers to take
cover and by that time they'd begun machine-
gunning the road all around you. For a minute
you stood there and looked around wildly. You expected to be hit any minute. Then you saw a wheat
field beyond a hedge at the right side of the road
and ploughed through the hedge and took a flat
dive into the wheat.

You lay there pressed face down in the dirt.
Machine-gun bullets were spatting down all
around you. You kept wriggling your helmet
around, trying to cover the back of your neck
and your forehead at the same time. And always
every minute you expected to feel a slug tear into

the back of your neck. Bombs began dropping out
in the field. You were absolutely sick with terror.
Then for some reason you looked around you and
the bottom fell out of your stomach for a minute.
The wheat was only about a foot high and there
you were spread-eagled out in it like a goddamned
target. You knew you had to get up and run and
you knew that never in your life were you going
to have anything harder to do. You took a couple
of deep breaths and mumbled some sort of prayer,
like a prize-fighter coming out of his corner at
the beginning of a fight.

Then you got up and ran. You scrambled up
the bank through the hedge. It was all thorns and
you cut up your hands. One of your guys was
hanging on to a tree at the side of the hedge. He
was green and shaking. He was frozen to the tree.
You hung to the tree a minute.

"Hey, Johnny," you yelled. "Where the hell are
you?"

"Down here getting drunk." His voice came
from somewhere along the hedge. You started for
him and wrenched the guy who was hanging to the
tree along with you.

O'Hara was huddled in the bottom of a ditch
next to the hedge. Most of his body was in the
hedge itself and only his head and shoulders stuck

out. He was on his side looking up at the planes and drinking from a long dark bottle. You flopped next to him and pulled the other guy down with you.

"Here." O'Hara gave you the bottle.

It looked like red wine and you took a terrific guzzle on it. It turned out to be *marc* and it almost strangled you, but from the minute that stuff hit the bottom of your stomach you were drunk and from the minute you were drunk you were all right again.

You were still holding the other guy's hand and his face was so sick with fear that you squeezed his hand as if he were a little kid and passed the bottle. When you squeezed his hand he tried to smile. He was in a bad way and so you kept holding his hand through the attack.

There were a lot of soldiers lying there in the hedge and they were scared to death, too.

But O'Hara was working on them. He kept passing the bottle around.

"Le bistro est maintenant ouvert," he said. "C'est ici le signe de la bombe. Le signe de la bonne bombe."

The planes were Italian and they were flying overhead in a circle. They were diving straight down until it seemed they would crash. Then you could see the little black ball that was the bomb drop from the plane and then boomf it would land. Some of the planes just flew up and down machine-gunning the road and fields and the ditches.

The machine-gun bullets just kept on riveting down all around you like hailstones and the bombs were landing with almost no interval.

A bomb landed in the field where you'd been lying. The dirt showered down crisply on your helmet.

"Jesus, Johnny," you said, "how the hell do the words to a Hail Mary go?"

You expected any minute to feel the trees come crashing down on top of you. You looked up, but the trees were still there. Dear Father in Heaven, you murmured, thank you, thank you very much. And you took another drink.

One of your people stood up on the other side of the road. The stuff was coming down all around him, but he just sauntered across the road with his hands in his pockets and when he got to you he sat down and worked his way calmly into the hedge.

"You sods," he said, "I had a marvelous place to stay over there."

"You should have stayed there," O'Hara said.

"I was lonely," he said. "Let's have a shot, Johnny."

O'Hara passed him the bottle. It was empty. You remembered that one of the soldiers in your car had brought some liquor with him. You were drunk then and felt very brave.

"Just a minute," you said. And you got up and walked out to your car. The minute you stood up you didn't feel so brave. It was one hell of a feeling having that stuff swishing down. You knew exactly how a bird must feel when you shoot at it. But you crouched and ran along the road to your car and looked in the back. There were about a dozen bottles of rum back there. You loaded your arms with bottles of rum and started back.

"Good show," said the guy who had come across the road.

"Oh, it was nothing," you said. "Nothing at all."

O'Hara snorted. "Stout fella," he sneered. "Tell us another story before you get knocked off."

"Shut up," you said.

"Well," he said, "this is what you were asking for, baby."

"This is damned fine rum," the guy who'd come across the road said.

"Volcanic ash," O'Hara said. "I read it in the

New Yorker. Here, give him some." He pointed to the guy whose hand you'd been holding.

The guy was better now, but he shivered as if he had a chill.

"Here," you said, "drink this."

He took a long swallow. "I'm sorry," he said. "I'm sorry I'm acting this way. I'm scared," he said, "I've never been so scared."

"Neither have I," O'Hara said.

He was passing bottles to the soldiers. Everyone was getting drunk. The soldiers were fine now. They began to loosen up and make themselves comfortable. The attack was still at full pitch.

"I'll bet one of those guys is the dago I socked five years ago in Tony's," O'Hara said. "I don't blame you for hating wops. I hate them too."

"I'll never speak to a wop again," you said. "They're a bunch of murdering yellow bastards."

"Dagos," you all started yelling. "Wop bastards, Spigs. Stinking lousy wops. Wops. Wops."

"When I get back to New York," O'Hara said, "I'm going to sock every wop I see. I hate their lousy guts. I hate them worse than Germans."

"Me, too," you said.

Everybody was really stinking drunk by then. Really stinking. It began to seem cozy in the hedge.

O'Hara began to sing *Tipperary*. The French

soldiers looked at him as if he was mad, but it cheered them up.

You laughed foolishly. It was like a movie or something you read about. Lying potted in a hedge with seventy-five Italians shooting the bejesus out of everything around you.

"I'm all right, now," the guy whose hand you'd held, said.

"Sure you are."

The guy who'd come across the road began to sing the *Whiffenpoof* song.

"Next to wops," O'Hara said. "I hate Yales." Then he went on singing. Now he was singing *Boomps a' Daisy* and the French soldiers were singing with him. After *Boomps a' Daisy* you sang *If You Were the Only Girl in the World* and then *When You Wore a Tulip*.

"If anybody sings *Workin' on the Railroad*, I hope he gets hit," O'Hara said.

The Italians were still there. Dirt kept showering down from the explosions in the wheat field.

"If those bastards knew what was going on down here," O'Hara said, "they'd die of fright."

Finally the attack was over and everybody stood out in the road. The whole section was plastered by that time, but everybody still knew what they

were doing. Two more cars and drivers were missing.

The section was bombed and machine-gunned
seven more times that day between Sezanne and
Nogent sur Seine. Sometimes you lay in ditches,
sometimes you were out in the woods, and sometimes you were on your belly in the fields and
always there were the bombs and the spat spat
riveting of the machine-guns. And always there
were those same moments of panicky terror at the
beginning of each attack. You were getting very
tired and very punch-drunk and very hard and
cold somewhere inside yourself.

The road had been full of refugees besides soldiers and the Italians had really given them hell.
There were many dead horses and wrecked farm
carts and the belongings of thousands of people
scattered around the roads. There were dead people also. There was a motorcycle with a dead man
slumped over the handle-bars and two dead children in the side-car. They were little girls. Little
blonde girls. They were about six years old. And
they had both been shot in the back.

At that moment with all your heart you asked
God's curse on all the child murderers in the
world.

Inside yourself you said something from a play

by Sean O'Casey. . . . "Mother Mary, take away their hearts of stone and give them hearts of flesh."

The Chasseur sergeant was humming *Sambre et Meuse,* but when he saw the dead children he stopped. "Pauvres petites," he said. Then he didn't talk any more.

Finally you came into Nogent sur Seine. It was packed with refugees. There were thousands of them, sitting wearily along the pavements or wandering along the street aimlessly and more of them were pouring into the town every minute. It was also packed with soldiers from every regiment in the army. They were milling around division headquarters. The rumor was that the army would make a stand here on the Seine. Watching these fragments of regiments come in, which were no more than bands of armed men, and unarmed men, made you think of the old days when the clans would gather in the hills. Except these were tired bleary men. But there were good regiments in that town. There were thousands of good soldiers there, but at headquarters they only told them to keep falling back. It was criminal.

Parachute mines were exploding in the river. Every time one went off the refugees moaned. You parked the cars and went to look for some place where you could all get hot food. You found a hotel with a cook in the kitchen and ordered dinner for everyone. You just walked into the kitchen and picked up what you wanted. Then you left a guy there to watch the cook while he fixed it. The guy told the cook that if any of that food was missing from the dinner he'd beat hell out of him. The streets were packed. You and O'Hara saw a child hobbling along on a bandaged foot. He was a little boy and he'd been hurt in an air raid about an hour before and they'd dressed his foot and now he was trying to get home. O'Hara picked him up and you carried him through back alleys to a poor little house where he lived.

The child's mother was standing at the door and when she saw the child she began to cry, but you explained that the little boy was all right and then when she found out you were Americans she asked you into the house. It was very clean inside and there was a holy picture with a light burning under it. O'Hara crossed himself.

The woman said you must have wine with her. You said no, but she brought out a bottle of cheap champagne and opened it and you all drank. The mines were still going off at regular intervals in the river. They made a terrific noise which never stopped. It was very nerve-racking.

"And this is the end of France," the woman

kept saying. "The end of France." The way she said it was the saddest thing you'd ever heard. And then you realized how you always had thought of France as something safe and solid and ever-lasting. You could imagine other countries going down and losing their freedom, but not France. That seemed as if it would have to be the end of everything and now it was happening.

"And this," the woman said, "is the war. This dirty thing. What do they think in America? Why don't they help us? Cannot they feel this? Don't they know that it isn't for power we ask this any-more? It is for our children and our homes. For boys like him." She pointed to the little boy. "Next it will be England," she said. "It isn't for money we ask this help. We ask them to save our chil-dren. Don't they know?"

You shook your heads. You didn't know the answer.

You had dinner finally, but it didn't taste good. Not with those mines going off in the river. Not with three of your cars and drivers missing in one day. You were still pretty drunk, too. But it wasn't your fault. It was necessary to be drunk. You couldn't do your job, sober. Not out there with those bombs. They blasted everything. Soldiers, civilians, towns, and chickens and ducks. There were many dead ducks. They lay around in the dust just like people. There were not so many dead geese. You guessed maybe geese were smarter than ducks. You went and found a bureau tabac and bought many packs of cigarettes and boxes of matches. You could hardly hear yourself talk with those mines going off. You were nervous and angry with everyone. You hated everyone, then. You could have even hated your own mother with those damned mines going off all the time.

You went into church to get out of the noise. It was dim and cool. There were refugees sleeping in the pews and on the floor in the aisles. One woman was moaning to herself and holding her stomach. You guessed maybe she was having a baby. You figured she'd come to the best place to have it. At first you felt out of place in the church with your helmet and your pistol, but then you began to feel relaxed. You asked Our Father to please get you out of the mess you'd volunteered yourself into and would He do the same for the rest of the section and please take care of all the refugees. You began to feel better. You were even a little cocky when you left the church.

You found that the others had bought up all

the chocolate and biscuits in the town and were
feeding the refugees. The refugees mobbed them,
fighting for the biscuits and the chocolate. Finally
there were no more in town.

You were told to report to Romilly sur Seine
and you started off. It was getting dark. Half-
way into Romilly you knew it was no use. The
place was on fire and there was shooting in the
town. The Germans had taken it. So you slanted
off on back roads toward Sens. For all you knew
you would have to sneak through the German
lines to get there. Along the roads you picked
up refugees. The two British soldiers were a great
help. They worked hard loading the ambulances.
So did the three Polish soldiers. The refugees were
loaded down with their belongings. You had to
make them leave most of that stuff behind. You had
to throw their things away in the fields. One old
man cried because he couldn't bring his bicycle.

That night you lay in the straw on the floor
of the cathedral at Sens. You couldn't sleep and
you tossed around. Then you felt someone's hand
on your shoulder. You jerked up. It was a young
priest. He was about twenty-five years old. His
face was gentle and very sad.

He patted your shoulder. "Soyez tranquille,

You came into the town tired and dirty. The town was unnaturally quiet, especially for towns in that district which was filled with the remnants of the Polish army. This, however, was a staff town. Except for yourselves there were no officers in town under the rank of major.

The other officers in the town were scrupulously clean. They wore tan linen summer tunics and dark trousers. You wore filthy tunics and grease-stained breeches. You needed to shave and to sleep. You needed to sober up. Your ambulances were battered and smashed. You had just come from the front. You were on your way to God knows where. These remnants of divisions were supposed to re-form and go back into the fighting. That was all you knew. Except that you were to have a night's decent sleep in rooms which had been assigned you. The rooms were wonderful. Clean with big feather beds. The house you were billeted in was owned by an old woman in a black skull cap. You introduced yourself to her.

"You speak French?" she said.

"My grandmother was French."

"Ah," she smiled. "And you have come home to fight."

"Something like that."

"That is good," she said.

Then she showed you to your room. Before she left it, she winked at you.

"This room is very quiet," she said. "I hear nothing. You understand." She wagged her head toward the village square where a group of girls stood around your ambulances.

"I am very tired, madame."

"You need to relax, mon aspirant."

"I need to sleep, madame."

She smiled. "Relaxation first. Sleep afterwards."

You bowed, smiling, as did she. Then you were alone in the first room with a bed you'd seen for weeks.

After you had washed and cleaned up as best you could you went down the stairs and across the square to the bistro which was to be the mess. On the way you stopped at the cars. Beside the cars there were many little boys in addition to the young girls.

"Tell me," one of the little boys said, "these are American cars?"

"Yes."

"From America?"

"Yes."

He turned triumphantly to the others. "See," he said, "what have I told you?" Then he turned back to me. "What is the speed?"

"One hundred and twenty kilometers."

"Par l'heure?"

"Par l'heure, mon gosse."

"That is good," he said gravely.

Another little boy approached me. He pointed to the side of your car. "You have really been at those places?" Written hastily on the side of the car were the words . . . Somme, Marne, Champagne, Seine.

"Yes, I have been there."

"You have seen the boche?"

"Not exactly. I have been in contact with them, but not exactly seen them."

"They are formidable, hein?"

You shrugged.

"They are more formidable than ours?"

"Nous verrons," you said.

"Ils verront," he laughed and the others joined in with him.

At the door to the bistro you met one of your drivers. "Christ," he said, "there's a general inside. What do we do?"

"Salute, I guess."

"I suppose that's all we can do."

"To hell with him," you said, "let's have a Pernod."

You went inside. The general was seated all

alone. He was a big man in a tan summer tunic and on his shoulders were the braid zig-zags of a Polish general. You stopped in the doorway and clicked your heels and saluted with two fingers to your berets in the Polish manner. He bowed gravely. Then you sat down and ordered Pernod.

Finally the others drifted in. It was amusing to see them come swaggering in, proudly self-conscious of their dirty uniforms, beards, red sleepless eyes, the real front-line look, and then see them stop short at the sight of this general. It seemed to amuse the general, too. But he returned each hastily formal salute gravely. It was the first general most of you had ever seen at such close quarters. You were practically dining with him. It was something to write home about.

You had a marvelous meal. Soup with noodles. Meat. Spaghetti. Salad. Red Wine. Fruit. It was wonderful. And afterwards you sat there drinking your coffee and brandy and talked, talked, talked. Loudly. Most of it for the benefit of the general.

"My God, I was in that ditch and one landed right in the field next to me."

"They machine-gunned the whole road around me."

"Me, too."

Then more Polish officers came into the room.

They all saluted the general and then sat at his table. They were mostly captains and majors. One of them was a colonel. He was also a priest. He sat at the general's right. The officers ate and drank much. They became very gay. Their conversation crackled and snarled in the Polish language. The woman who ran the bistro was very busy serving both tables, theirs and yours.

Some young men in civilian clothes came in and sat at an adjoining table to yours. They drank red wine and talked politics in loud voices. They made low-voiced remarks about the Polish officers in French and then laughed very loudly. They were not young men of the village. They spoke with Paris accents. One of your people went over to them and spoke to them. When he came back his face was grave.

"They've evacuated Paris," he said. "These guys just got here. They've made Paris an open city. Surrendered it."

The general heard you mention Paris and sent one of his captains to your table. You all stood up stiffly.

"You have news of Paris?" he asked in that Polish French which sounds so much like the French of the Midi.

"Yes, sir. Paris has been declared an open city.

It has been evacuated. These young men have just come from there."

"Thank you, mes aspirants."

He went back and told the news to the general. The general looked over in our direction and bowed his thanks for our information. Then he looked at his watch and sent one of his officers to turn on the radio.

Everyone stopped talking as this officer fiddled with the dials and tuned his way through the static to the French official news broadcast.

The news broadcast was brief. Pétain himself spoke. He spoke in an old man's rotting voice. France would surrender he said. She could no longer go on fighting. Then they played the *Marseillaise*. Everyone stood up. Straighter than ever. Defiantly almost, as they played the song. Everyone avoided everyone else's eyes. Then just as the song was over and you were about to sit down, the general rapped against his glass with a spoon, and haltingly in a tuneless voice he began to sing and one by one the officers joined with him in the Polish national anthem.

When they finished the priest suddenly went down on his knees and began to pray. Everyone remained standing as the priest prayed for Poland. He prayed to God to protect the Polish soldiers who stood alone now. As he finished everyone, more or less, looked down at the floor and said his own private prayer.

Then there was another announcement over the radio. It said that although France was no longer fighting a state of war still existed between Poland and the Third German Reich. And that the Polish troops at the Maginot Line were still fighting.

The Polish officers cheered. All except the general and the priest. The general made a short announcement in Polish and left the room. The priest followed him. The officers settled down at the table and began to drink brandy. Then they began to sing. They sang beautifully. They sang many Polish folk songs. Then they asked you would you sing them some American or English songs. There was nothing else you could do. So you sang *Tipperary* for them. When you finished they clapped loudly and made you have drinks with them. After that you felt you wanted to sing. You sang many songs for them and they sang for you. It was very gay. You were all very drunk.

It was late that night when you arrived back at your billet. You had been ordered to try and sleep for a while, but not to undress. You must be ready at any moment to begin evacuating the Polish troops toward Bordeaux and Saint Jean de Luz to embark them for England. As for yourselves, you did not know what your status was. You were Americans, but you were also Polish officers. You did not know whether you were still at war or at peace.

The old lady who owned the house was standing out in front when you arrived. She was watching a stream of refugees go by.

"You know?" she asked you when you got there.

"Yes, madame."

"It is a crime," she said. "A crime and a shame. Pétain is a traitor. He should go to the guillotine. I should like to see him there."

A high farm cart came by. It was loaded with children and with furniture. The driver was an old man. He was singing in a toneless, hopeless voice. He was singing *La Normandie, C'est Mon Pays.*

Then many people on foot. Farmers leading live-stock and carts upon which their families sat.

The old lady stiffened. "Turn back," she said to them. "Turn back and fight. Go back and fight." She shouted and there was stifled sobbing in her voice. "Go back," she shouted again, "go back and fight."

There was no answer. Only the sad sound of the

first man singing off in the distance. *La Normandie, C'est Mon Pays*.

The next morning you had breakfast in a little bistro many miles away toward Bordeaux. It was filled with wandering French soldiers. Most of them were from the front. They sat silently. They were very tired and very dirty. There was a big sign on the wall advertising armament bonds. Souscrivez, it said, Nous Sommes les Plus Puissants.

Suddenly one of the French soldiers stood up. He had many ribbons on his tunic. The Croix de Guerre and the Medaille Militaire and the Medaille des Blessés. He stood there looking at the poster and then he picked up his coffee cup and threw it at the poster. The cup smashed and the coffee trickled down over the paper.

The soldier sat down again weakly and put his head on the table. He was crying.

It was all finished. Everything was irrevocably over. Everything was utterly lost.